The Little R

The Life and Times of an
East Yorkshire Doctor

By

John K Gosnold

With

Margaret Garbett

Hutton Press
2003

Published by

The Hutton Press Ltd.,
130 Canada Drive, Cherry Burton,
Beverley, East Yorkshire
HU17 7SB

Printed by

Image Colourprint,
Willerby, Hull
HU10 6EB

ISBN 1 902709 21 7

CONTENTS

DEDICATION
To Kathleen – for saving my life.

Acknowledgements

My thanks –

To Margaret Garbett, whom I have come to know and love over the last five years, and whom I hope I have also been able to support in times of stress. She has become a great friend.

To all the people I have mentioned in this book, some of whom are prepared for it, some of whom will be surprised.

To Uncle Len and Auntie Molly for the huge amount of family history they have been able to share with me. They have waited a long time for this book.

To other members of my family for information and photographs.

To those whom I have not mentioned and who might be disappointed – they will be in the next one!

To anyone to whom I may have caused offence I apologise.

John Gosnold, Lelley, East Yorkshire

I would like to add my thanks –

To John himself for his patience and good humour as I questioned his memories and researched ancestors he didn't know he had.

To Kath, who so gracefully effaced herself as John and I poured over our computers and clogged up each other's phones with faxes and who supported both of us throughout.

To the staff of the Hull Daily Mail for allowing me access to their archives.

To Judith Elsdon of the American Museum in Claverton, near Bath, for similar facilities.

To Helen Greensides and Steve Massam of BBC Radio Humberside for checking the memories of John and myself.

To my family for their unfailing belief in me.

Finally to Charles and Dae Brook of Hutton Press, my friends for twenty years, who have always supported my efforts. Dae tragically died very suddenly during the production of this book.

Margaret Garbett, Winsley, Bradford-on-Avon, Wiltshire.

(Some names have been changed for legal reasons and to protect the subjects' families.)

PROLOGUE

The scene had the unreality of a stage set from Alice in Wonderland. All I could see was a fireman straight ahead of me looking down the railway carriage which had toppled onto its side, while others worked through broken windows to free passengers trapped in the ditch beneath it.

The only useful job I could do was to *'confirm death'* as they retrieved bodies and parts of bodies. Perhaps the saddest find was a pregnant woman with severe abdominal injuries.

At one stage I had to squeeze through a broken window, crawl under the coach and into the ditch and then work my way along it. It was extremely hot, dirty and distressing and I found myself wondering if this was what I had been trained for – if this was what I had envisaged all those years ago as a young lad in Hornsea when I had first thought about being a doctor.

The Lockington train disaster was the first event of this magnitude to which the relatively new Hull Royal Infirmary Flying Squad had been summoned by the Ambulance Service, and only the second major incident where, as Accident and Emergency Consultant, I had been in charge.

My medical career had been very varied since I had qualified in 1965 – over twenty years of ministering to the sick in body and mind. Now I was performing a task which to all intents and purposes amounted to an admission of defeat. There was nothing more anyone could do for the victims of the horrific crash which had so abruptly shattered the peaceful summer countryside near this pretty East Yorkshire village.

I gave myself a mental shake and carried on along the ditch. There was plenty more for me to do. Now was not the time to indulge in introspection. Later maybe, when I had the leisure, I would pause and take stock of my life and attempt to find out how I came to be here, under a derailed train, in a fair amount of personal danger, looking for signs of life and pronouncing death on complete strangers.

Family Tree of the Gosnold's

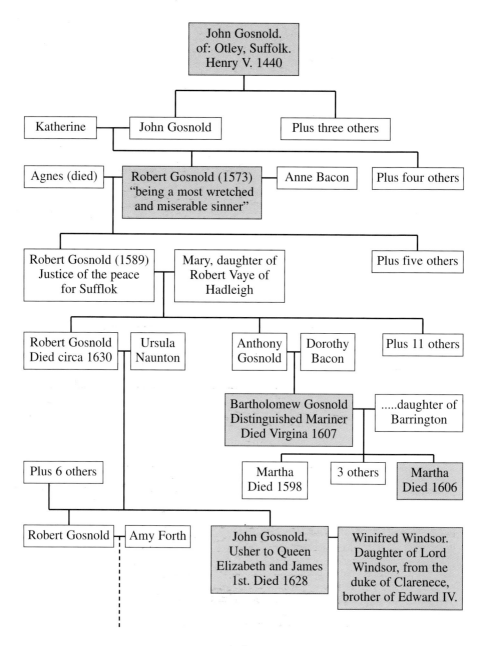

John Gosnold.
of: Otley, Suffolk.
Henry V. 1440

Katherine — John Gosnold — Plus three others

Agnes (died) — Robert Gosnold (1573)
"being a most wretched
and miserable sinner" — Anne Bacon — Plus four others

Robert Gosnold (1589)
Justice of the peace
for Sufflok — Mary, daughter of
Robert Vaye of
Hadleigh — Plus five others

Robert Gosnold
Died circa 1630 — Ursula
Naunton — Anthony
Gosnold — Dorothy
Bacon — Plus 11 others

Bartholomew Gosnold
Distinguished Mariner
Died Virgina 1607 — .....daughter of
Barrington

Plus 6 others — Martha
Died 1598 — 3 others — Martha
Died 1606

Robert Gosnold — Amy Forth — John Gosnold.
Usher to Queen
Elizabeth and James
1st. Died 1628 — Winifred Windsor.
Daughter of Lord
Windsor, from the
duke of Clarenece,
brother of Edward IV.

Continuation of Family Tree

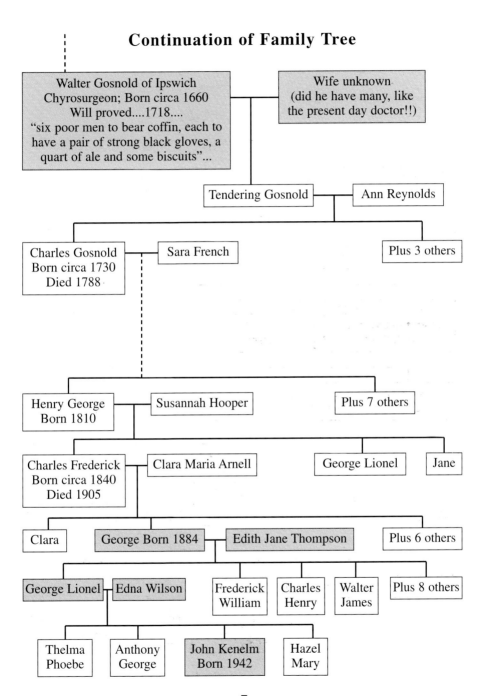

Walter Gosnold of Ipswich Chyrosurgeon; Born circa 1660 Will proved....1718.... "six poor men to bear coffin, each to have a pair of strong black gloves, a quart of ale and some biscuits"...

Wife unknown (did he have many, like the present day doctor!!)

Tendering Gosnold — Ann Reynolds

Charles Gosnold Born circa 1730 Died 1788 — Sara French

Plus 3 others

Henry George Born 1810 — Susannah Hooper

Plus 7 others

Charles Frederick Born circa 1840 Died 1905 — Clara Maria Arnell

George Lionel

Jane

Clara

George Born 1884 — Edith Jane Thompson

Plus 6 others

George Lionel — Edna Wilson

Frederick William

Charles Henry

Walter James

Plus 8 others

Thelma Phoebe

Anthony George

John Kenelm Born 1942

Hazel Mary

ANCESTORS

A mixed bag of Gosnolds, dating back literally to the time of William the Conqueror, since when they have travelled the world in the service of their sovereign and their country, 'discovered' and named Cape Cod and Martha's Vineyard and in turn have had places named after them.

Duke plays a round to recover lost colony.

The Duke of York and President Clinton played golf together yesterday and decided to spice up their game by placing a bet on the result. Their wager was the entire island of Martha's Vineyard, one of the most expensive and exclusive pieces of real estate in America. Dukes of York were hereditary owners of Martha's Vineyard in the 17th century, but it went the way of all England's colonies in 1776.

"If he beats me we have to give him back the island," said Mr Clinton.

"Do you want the island back sir?" the Duke was asked.

"I'll tell you when I've won," he replied.

But the White House spin doctors were already wondering whether the result should remain a state secret. There was indeed no word of who won.

Extract from an article by Hugo Gurdon in a Washington newspaper in September 1999.

It has been a fascinating and sometimes painful process piecing together my family history. During the search I think – I hope – I have begun to know myself better. I have been forced to sort out fact from family mythology and to discuss things – feelings, memories – with my immediate family which we would probably never have talked about otherwise. Also, as I promised myself thirteen years ago, I have taken stock of my career and my personal life and tried to put things into perspective. This book is an attempt to put into context many of the advances in medicine which have occurred during the last thirty years or so and to set them against a family whose history has at times been colourful and at others as mundane as millions of others.

I have been able to trace the Gosnold family tree back to the fifteenth century when a John Gosnold (or Gosnell – the name has a variety of spellings through the centuries) lived in Clopton near the little village of Otley, but the origins of the family are well documented in the time of William the Conqueror. In 1066 a knight called Arnold came to England with King William's trusted advisor Lanfranc, who was granted land near Canterbury in Kent. He in turn housed his knights in local manor houses.

Arnold was given the manor of a Saxon named Gosa and for the purposes of the Domesday Book in 1086 was known as Arnold de Gosa, or Arnold of Gosa's Hall, corrupted over the years to Gosnold, or in the case of the Irish branch of the family in the 1700's, Gosnell. The original Gosnolds left Kent for Suffolk in 1228.

The John at the top of my traceable family tree died in 1470 and was connected in some way with King Henry V. His son Robert sold the Clopton property to Thomas Rous and it has been known as Rous Hall ever since. It is surmised that with part of the proceeds he built Otley Hall. Otley lies on the Debenham road, 8 miles north east of Ipswich and 6 miles north west of Woodbridge, in the rolling, well-wooded Suffolk landscape. Otley Hall itself is on a narrow road leading northward from the village, halfway between Helmingham and Clopton, and is one of the finest and best preserved Grade I Listed timber-framed medieval houses in East Anglia. The original building, a simple plastered house, is now the kitchen wing and it was Robert Gosnold and his wife Agnes Hill of Ashe who in around 1500, obviously having prospered, built a new range of rooms at right angles to the first. These included a hall with carved and moulded beams, the walls clad in oak linenfold panelling. In the middle of the sixteenth century Otley Hall was extended again by another Robert, with a new wing being thrown out to the north. It is said that the ground floor included a timber colonnade, used for bowling and cockfighting, whilst in 1559, to celebrate a family wedding, the upstairs banqueting room was painted with trompe-l'oeil panelling and coats of arms, some of which still survive. Partly moated and with 10 acres of fine gardens in need of restoration, it was on the market in 1996 for £750,000. The new owners, the poet and philosopher Mr Hagger and his wife Ann, sympathetically restored both house and garden, adding a tennis court and swimming pool. For the last 20 years the house, with its display recounting its history, has been open to the public on selected days. In September 2002, four hundred years after Bartholomew Gosnold first sailed for America, it was once more on the market for offers in excess of £2.5 million.

The Royal connections continue when in 1553 the Manor of Witnesham, just 3 or 4 miles from Otley, was granted by King Edward VI to Edward Nevill who in 1558 *'had licence to alienate the same to Robert Gosnold sen. and Robert Gosnold jun. The sale was effected by fine levied in 1559 between Robert Gosnold and others and the said Edward Nevill and others'*.

Robert Gosnold senior was the great great grandson of the fifteenth century John. Robert's father, also Robert, was a JP for Suffolk and his uncle, another John Gosnold, was MP for Ipswich in 1547 and again in 1553 when he was appointed Solicitor General. Lord Campbell, in Volume 2 of his 'Lives of Chancellors of England' writes that *'A short time before the death of Edward VI, when Northumberland's object was to obtain from the King a change in the succession in favour of Lady Jane Grey, Gryffyth, the Attorney General, opposed the plan and though the Judges at last agreed to it on certain conditions, the arrangement was not satisfactory to Gosnold, the Solicitor General, but means were found to bring him over the next day.'*

What means, one wonders? Whatever, he died the next year, without issue.

When Robert Gosnold senior, who had inherited Otley Hall from his grandfather, died in 1616 the Manor of Witnesham passed to his cousin and heir, yet another Robert and on his death in 1638 went to a Robert Gosnold for the final time. By 1650 it was in the possession of a family by the name of Edgar.

A century earlier when Edmund Gosnold died in 1540 instructions were given for *'1 Comb of Wheat to be baken, 1 Comb of Malt to be brewed and 3 Sheep to be baken on his burial day'*. Obviously quite an occasion and not unlike my own approach to my inevitable demise. I would prefer people to celebrate my past life and all the good things in it rather than get too morbid over the fact that I am no longer with them. I would quite like a horse and cart and a New Orleans style jazz band to feature in my funeral.

The Gosnold family, who all seemed to have numerous offspring, (a family trait carried on even into this century) were prominent landowners and public figures throughout the area and owned many of the estates and manor houses. While retaining Otley Hall Robert senior, himself one of eleven children, had sold Rous Hall in Clopton when he bought Witnesham. He and his wife, Ursula Naunton, had four sons and four daughters. One son, yet another John, born in 1568, was a Gentleman Usher to Queen Elizabeth and James I and a Gentleman of the Privy Chamber to Charles I. He died in 1628 aged 60 and there is a fulsome memorial to him in St Mary's Church in Otley.

Here Resteth interred the body of Iohn Gosnold Esq. 3d: Sonne of Robert Gosnold of Otley Esq, and Ursula his wife, borne of the right antient & wor: families of Naunton & Wingfield of Letheringham. His tender yeares in good studies at Oxford & London his riper years hee spent in Court where he served in the place of gentle-man Usher in ordinary the Maties. of Q: ELIZABETH and K IAMES 26 yeares. & was after a gentleman of ye privy chamber in ordinarie to K: CHARLES. He married Winifred Ye daughter of Walter Windsor Esq. 3. sonne of William Lo: Windsor & of Margaret his wife, daughter of Sr. Geffrey Poole Knight sonne of Sr. Richard Poole Kt. and the Lady Margarett Countesse of Salisbury his wife, daughter of the right noble

Prince George Duke of Clarence, Brother to K: Edward the fourth of England. He departed this life the 17TH. of February Anno Dmi: 1628. aged 60 yeares. who had issue by his said wife 5 sonnes and 3 daughters. to whos memory his said wife caused this Inscription to be erected.

Not only were Winifred's spelling and punctuation a bit dodgy but she was obviously determined to point out her own royal connections in addition to her husband's.

John's eldest brother – yet another Robert – married Amy Forthe of Otley and their eldest son – inevitably Robert again – married Anne, daughter of Sir Lionel Talmac, or Tollemache, of Helmingham, 1st Baronet, in 1609. The next Robert, who was baptised at Helmingham in May 1611, was described as a *'gent. of Otley, Suffolk'* when as a bachelor of 22, with his father's consent, he married Dorothy Jeggon of Westminster, spinster, aged 17, daughter of the late Right Rev. Bishop of Norwich. She had the consent of her mother, Dame Dorothea Cornwallis. Dame Dorothea's father had been Bishop of Bangor, then Chester and finally London. After the death of her first husband she married Sir Charles Cornwallis. Robert and Dorothy were married at St Martin-in-the-Fields, London, by Licence dated February 1632/3. Robert was *'a most loyal Gentleman and gallant Officer'* and served His Majesty King Charles I against his rebellious Parliament. As a Colonel of Foot in the Royalist Army he defended Carlisle for a considerable time but after the Battle of Naseby it was surrendered on 25th June 1645. It was taken again by the Royalists in 1648 but when the Civil War was near its close the city finally surrendered to Oliver Cromwell. Troublous times for the Gosnolds.

The family obviously survived, although they were fined so heavily for their loyalty to King Charles I that by about 1700 Lionel, who was rector of Otley as well as Squire, had to sell the Hall and the Estate to the Rebow family, who owned it for the next 200 years. Lionel's brother, Walter, was a surgeon in Ipswich and obviously a gentleman of some consequence as at his funeral in 1718 there were *'Six poor men to bear the coffin, each to have a pair of strong black gloves, a quart of ale and some biskitts'*. It is to be hoped that they were duly grateful and that they quaffed the ale after rather than before bearing the coffin! (I must remember to specify some liquid refreshment for the jazz band.)

It was from this Walter through a succession of further Roberts, Lionels, Walters and Thomases that we come to Thomas Gosnold, Freeman of Norwich, 1786-1850. He had four four sons and one daughter. His middle son, Henry George, married Susannah Hooper and their second son, Charles

11

Frederick, married Clara Maria Arnall and broke away from three centuries of East Anglian occupation by moving south, first to Hertfordshire and then to London, to New Southgate to be precise. There we will leave them briefly while we return to the late sixteenth century and the Robert Senior who acquired Witnesham manor. His younger brother, Anthony, lived at Grundisburgh with his wife Dorothy Bacon, two sons and five daughters. Their eldest son, Bartholomew, born in either 1571 or 1572, is described in the family tree as a *'distinguished Mariner'* – probably the understatement of the year. He was in fact one of the foremost mariners of all time. His father eventually sold the Grundisburgh estate and moved to Norwich.

Following family tradition Bartholomew was educated at Cambridge from where he matriculated as a 'pensioner' of Jesus College in 1587 but there is no mention of him taking a degree. Details of his life before he became a mariner are rather sparse but it is thought he may have practiced law before going to sea in 1596, by which time he would have been about 25. A year earlier he had married Mary Golding, second daughter of Martha Golding, said by some reference books to be his aunt. (A couple of American biographical dictionaries have him married in 1596 to a 'Catherine Barrington, daughter of Sir Thomas Barrington'. We will assume however that by a majority vote he was married to Mary Golding.)

Through his mother-in-law he was related to Sir Thomas Smythe, through his mother to Sir Francis Bacon and through his father to Sir John Gilbert (who married his aunt) and to Edward Maria Wingfield. Not to mention his cousin John, firmly ensconced at the court of Queen Elizabeth I. All of these family connections were to play an important part in his future.

According to his contemporaries Bartholomew Gosnold was largely responsible for the colonisation of North America by the English but his work has gone mostly unrecognised, his reputation eclipsed by those of Drake, Gilbert, Raleigh and Smith. This may be because of his early death and the self-promotion of Captain John Smith of Pocohontas fame, but it was Gosnold's influence which kept the Jamestown experiment going against all the odds and he in fact led a party to what is now New England some four years before the infamous John Smith arrived.

The story starts between 1578 and 1583 when Sir Humphrey Gilbert, a kinsman by marriage of Bartholomew Gosnold, obtained a patent from Queen Elizabeth I for discovery and colonisation in north west America. He made a voyage to what was known as the New World in 1578 but his plan to establish a colony as a base against Spain, which itself was busy trying to colonise what is now Florida, had to wait for more financial support and he sailed home in

1579. He managed to raise some more money in Bristol and Southampton and sailed off again in June 1583 with five ships and 260 men. He reached Newfoundland and made some exploratory trips but his vessel was lost in September on its homeward journey.

Later that same year Admiral Sir Francis Drake sailed around South America and put into a bay at the 38th parallel. According to his ship's log he *'ordered divine service to be performed at his tent'*. This is thought to be the first Protestant service to be held in the New World.

In 1584 Sir Walter Raleigh, who was half-brother to Sir Humphrey Gilbert and had been a member of his first expedition, was granted a renewal of his patent and with the help of Walsingham, Drake, Sidney and two Richard Hakluyts - father and son - he equipped an expedition under the command of Sir Richard Grenville and Ralph Lane. They were to explore the North American Mainland and reconnoitre the Spanish Caribbean defences. After achieving the latter the expedition entered Albemarle Sound on the North Carolina coast and landed at Roanoke Island in July before returning to England in mid-September. Raleigh named his discovery 'Virginia' in honour of his beloved Queen and despatched a colonising expedition in April 1585 under the same commanders. They landed at Roanoke Island in July and Grenville left Lane in charge while he returned to England for fresh supplies but there was trouble with the aboriginal Indians and with the Spanish and the colony was abandoned in 1586 when Drake, who was passing by after a raid on the Spanish West Indies, offered the settlers passage home. When Grenville returned with the supplies a few weeks later he found the island deserted and left fifteen of his men there to try to start again.

In 1587 a fourth expedition set sail under John White, who was also an artist and who drew the local Indians playing lacrosse, practising archery, running races and pitching balls at a target at the top of a high tree. One of the Indians, Manteo, was baptised by the settlers into the Church of England and became the first aboriginal Indian to be converted to Protestant Christianity. In the same year the first English child was born in North America. She was Virginia Dare, and her parents were Ananais and Ellinor Dare. Ellinor was John White's daughter but he sailed for England to obtain supplies only a week after his grandaughter's birth. His return to the Island was delayed by the Spanish Armada and when he did finally reach Roanoke again three years later in August 1590 he found no trace of the colonists.

It is thought that there were about a million aboriginal Indians living in North America around 1600 when European colonisation really began. By 1602 plans were being made for another expedition to the New World, where it was hoped to find a passage through the American continent to the South Seas. It was to be led by Captain Edward Hayes, commander of one of Sir Humphrey Gilbert's ships, but for some reason the project was handed over to Bartholomew Gosnold. He was able to obtain financial support from Sir Thomas Smythe, nephew of his mother-in-law, Martha Golding and from Henry Wryothesly, Third Earl of Southampton through his family connections with Southampton's close friend the Earl of Essex. He sailed for Virginia from either Falmouth or Dartmouth (accounts differ) on the Concord on March 26th 1602. He was accompanied by thirty-two would-be settlers and was in command of both the ship and the expedition. At that time all the east coast of North America from Florida to Canada was known as Virginia. It was intended that Gosnold should remain behind with twenty settlers while Bartholomew Gilbert, a relative of the late Sir Humphrey and who was listed in the log as a Captain, would command the Concord on the return journey.

The outward voyage took forty-nine days and was the first to be made without putting in to the West Indies. This seems to have been somewhat inadvertent as a contemporary account by expedition member John Brereton explains.

'Captain Gosnoll, with 32 and himself in a small Barke, set sayle from Dartmouth upon the 26 of March. Though the wind favoured us not much at the first, but forced us as far Southward as the Azores, which was not much out of our way; we ran directly west from there, whereby we made our journey shorter than heretofore by 500 leagues. The weakness of our ship, the badnes of our saylers, and the ignorance of the coast, caused us to carry but a low sayle, that made our passage longer than we expected.'

The party made landfall at Savage Rock, probably the present Cape Neddich in Maine, on May 11th. It was described as being *'somewhat low with hummocks or hills, white sand on the shore, but very rockie and overgrown with fayre trees'*. They anchored and immediately a party of eight aboriginal Indians drew alongside in a small boat with mast and sail and *'came boldly aboard us'*. Although they were friendly Captain Gosnold decided not to go ashore as there wasn't a good harbour and the weather was not good either, so they weighed anchor and sailed on southward. The next morning they *'found themselves imbayed with a mightie headland'*. They anchored again and Bartholomew Gosnold, John Brereton and three others went ashore in a small boat. Although it was very hot they marched to the highest point from where they could see that the headland was in fact part of the mainland, with islands on its other side. They returned to the Concord and sailed round the headland where they caught more cod than they knew what

14

to do with. They initially named the area 'Gosnold's Hope', subsequently to be known as 'Cape Cod'.

They continued sailing south, then west, until they had rounded the group of islands, by one of which they anchored. It was uninhabited and about four miles in circumference. It was overgrown with trees, bushes and vines, there were strawberries, gooseberries and other fruits, herons and *'divers other sorts of fowle'*. Captain Gosnold called it 'Martha's Vineyard' after his little daughter who had died in 1598 when she was only a year old. The name was eventually transferred to a much bigger island, which still bears it today and which is known worldwide through its tragic connections with the Kennedy family. In 1969 Senator Edward Kennedy, brother of the assassinated President John F Kennedy, drove off the Chappaquiddick bridge on the island after a party and although he escaped uninjured his companion drowned. Exactly thirty years later in July 1999 John F Kennedy Junior, the late President's only son, was piloting his plane on the way to his cousin's wedding, with his wife and her sister as passengers, when they crashed into the sea. He had intended landing on Martha's Vineyard to drop off his sister-in-law before flying on to the Kennedy family's holiday home in nearby Hyannis Port. The original Martha's Vineyard is now No Man's Land.

As the settlers explored the other islands they met many of the local Indians but couldn't see where they lived. The Indians were friendly and gave them fish and tobacco. Eventually they arrived at an island which had so many creeks and coves that it seemed as though it was many small islands linked by bridges. This was the present day Cuttyhunk which they at that time named Elizabeth Island. It was grassy, with fruits and berries in abundance and they decided to establish themselves there for the time being. They planted wheat, barley and peas which *'in 14 dayes sprung up 9 ynches'*. Brereton describes the soil as *'fat and lusty'*. There were oak trees, cedars, beech, holly, walnut and hazel, and cherries with stalks bearing fruit *'like a cluster of Grapes, fortie or fiftie in a bunch'*. There was also a tree he couldn't identify *'of orange colour with a bark as smooth as velvet'*.

A lake of fresh water, some three miles round (now known as 'Gosnold's Pond'), had an island in its middle of an acre or thereabouts, overgrown with trees, where there were many tortoises. An abundance of *'all sorts of foules'* provided them with fresh meat and there were ground nuts as big as eggs *'as good as potatoes and 40 on a string, not two ynches under ground'*. Brereton waxes lyrical about the shellfish - *'Schalops, Mussels, Cockles, Crabs, Lobsters, Welks, Oysters, exceeding good and very great'*.

Moving on from this paradise they landed on the mainland which they found equally beautiful. *'We stood for a while as ravished at the beautie and dilicacy of the sweetnesse, besides divers cleare lakes, whereof we saw no end, & meadows very large and full of greene grass &e.'* There was a good harbour, despite the rocky shoreline, but as evening was drawing in they returned to the ship and thence to Elizabeth Island and the rest of the party they had left there. They spent three weeks building a house on the island in the lake, trading knives, hatchets, beads and bells for furs – beaver, martin, fox and wild cat – and lizard skins with the local Indians. Brereton notes that they had charms, collars and drinking cups made out of copper which they were happy to exchange for trinkets and they indicated that they took the metal out of the earth in Maine. The Indians stayed with them three days, retiring a few miles off each night, then most of them left, leaving behind seven men who helped Gosnold and his party with the digging and the carrying of sassafras, a tree whose fragrant root was used for flavouring and as the basis for an antiseptic used in the treatment of syphilis.

Gosnold and some of the settlers had intended staying there but in the end they decided that everyone should return to England as they didn't have enough provisions to last the six months that it would take Gilbert to sail home, obtain supplies and sail back again. They had thought that they would be able to set up a regular trade with the Indians for their everyday needs but this proved to be impossible. Bartholomew Gilbert was blamed for the fact that the supplies they had brought with them were inadequate and he was accused of misappropriating the money. Concord sailed for England on 18th June 1602 and reached Exmouth on 23rd July carrying furs, cedar and sassafras from Cuttyhunk. A furious Sir Walter Raleigh, who claimed a monopoly on all imports from North America, asked his friend Lord Cecil for help in confiscating the cargo. The outcome is not recorded! It has been suggested that Gosnold served under Raleigh on one or more of his expeditions but this is unlikely as Gosnold's kinsmen, Henry and Robert, had close ties with the Earl of Essex who was Raleigh's bitter enemy and there are indications that Raleigh considered Gosnold's 1602 voyage *'a grievous infringement'* of his American patent and Gosnold himself as an interloper. This may be one of the reasons why Bartholomew has been largely ignored by British historians, although he is much revered in America.

On their return to England John Brereton and his fellow traveller Gabriel Archer prepared *'favourable narratives'* of the voyage, Brereton's being published in that same year. Gosnold then set about trying to interest English merchants and financiers, including the influential Sir Ferdinando Gorge, in backing an American settlement. He was living in Bury St Edmunds at the

16

time with his wife Mary and five of his six children, who were all baptised in Bury church between 1597 and 1605. By 1606 he had managed to gather together enough money – or at least the promise of it – to finance another expedition. It was to be under the auspices of two companies, one based in London, the other in Plymouth. The Earl of Southampton, one of the backers of his original expedition, was still involved. In fact in 1605, the year of the arrest of Guy Fawkes for his part in the Gunpowder Plot, the Earl and his Roman Catholic son-in-law, Sir Thomas Arundel, had despatched George Weymouth to North America to establish a colony for Catholics, who were finding their position in England increasingly insecure, Catholic priests having been banished in 1604. Weymouth returned in July 1606 and his account of his voyage to Nantucket and the coast of Maine prompted two interrelated groups of merchants from London and Plymouth, ten of whom had backed John White's expedition of 1587, to petition King James for a new patent. This was conferred in 1606 and under its terms two 'Virginia Companies' were established, the London or South Virginia Company, authorised to settle in a region between latitudes 34 and 41 degrees North (where New York City is today) and the Plymouth or North Virginia Company which was allocated the land between 38 and 45 degrees North (site of the present day Washington). Neither was to settle within 100 miles of the other but each was to receive all lands 50 miles north and south of their first settlement and 100 miles into the interior.

The Charter provided for a Council of thirteen to be set up in the new colony, which would be directed by a Royal Council of thirteen back in England. The colonial council would select one of its members as president, who would have two votes, and it would have the power to make laws, impose taxes, mint money and dispense justice. Settlers would be granted all the liberties and privileges they enjoyed at home, including the right to own land and be tried by a jury. All taxes would be ploughed back into the economy of the colony. This was a great advance on former ideas, which had been solely concerned with grabbing the land and making money out of it, but nobody seems to have considered the wishes of the aboriginal Indians in the arrangement.

It was in fact the London Company which eventually financed the 1606 expedition. Queen Elizabeth, Gosnold's original backer, was dead and King James I of England, VI of Scotland, was on the throne, but he retained the ambitions of the Virgin Queen with regard to North America. Sir Francis Bacon, a relative of Bartholomew Gosnold's and soon to be Lord Chancellor of England, had given considerable thought to the matter. He decried the get-rich-quick motives of some of the backers and said it would take twenty years to establish a colony. The settlers, he said, should be selected for their special skills and should include many farmers so that the colony could become self-sufficient.

One of the grantees of the London-based Virginia Company was Edward Maria Wingfield, another relative of Bartholomew Gosnold, and Anthony Gosnold, his brother, was a subscriber to the stock. They both accompanied him when he set sail down the Thames from Blackwall in London on 20th December 1606. Captain Gosnold was in command of the God Speed, which carried fifty-two pioneers bound for the projected settlement. The God Speed was one of a fleet of three ships under the overall command of Captain Christopher Newport. Each had its hold crammed with tools, weapons, ammunition, food and grain. In all there were 105 pioneers, but despite Sir Francis Bacon's warnings most of them were classed as 'gentlemen' in the ship's log, including Bartholomew's cousin Anthony as well as his brother, and George Percy, brother of the Earl of Northumberland. There were however some skilled craftsmen - jewellers, goldsmiths, a perfumer, four carpenters, a blacksmith, a barber, a bricklayer, a mason, a tailor, sundry farmers and labourers and two surgeons, one classed as a gentleman, one not! Last on the list was Samuel Collier, boy. All shared one ambition - the hope of a better life than they presently had.

The God Speed also carried a sealed box containing the names of the councillors nominated by the Company and the instructions drawn up by the King's Council, including advice on agriculture and on how to deal with the Indians. Also, despite the progressive ideas in the Charter, the Company instructed the colonial council to search for gold and other precious metals, explore the rivers for the still elusive Northwest Passage to the South Seas and to look for Raleigh's lost colony. The box was not to be opened until the expedition reached Virginia.

Goodness knows why they chose to set sail in December. They only got as far as the Kent coast before meeting stormy weather and they had to anchor there for six weeks. The voyage was still as hazardous as when Gosnold had sailed out four years previously. God Speed was only 40 tons, the Susan Constant was roomier at 100 tons but the Pinnace Discovery was a mere 20 tons. They were aiming to reach the West Indies in four weeks where they would buy fruit and vegetables and pick up fresh water. Until then they would have to make do with salt meat, fish and biscuits once their limited supplies of fresh food ran out. The chaplain, Robert Hunt, who was only 20 miles from his home, became very ill, but instead of complaining or demanding to be taken off he kept urging his fellow sufferers to hang on. There were in fact quite a few who tried to persuade the captains to give up the expedition and go home.

The wind didn't ease until February 1907 when the little fleet eventually set sail, calling in at the Canaries for fresh water and trading with the islanders in Dominica. They arrived in Martinique on 23rd March and stayed there for about three weeks, recovering from their ordeal on a voyage which had by then taken three times as long as anticipated. Already they were experiencing strange new sights and sounds. According to a contemporary report, in Guadelope they found *'a bath so hot, as in it we boyled Porck as well as over a fire'*.

In early April they set off once again, passing by Puerto Rico and landing on a tiny island called Mona, where remarkably they suffered their first fatality with the death of Edmund Brooke. On the nearby island of Monica they discovered thousands of birds' eggs and carried two boat-loads back to the ships to supplement their meagre diet and *'tooke from the bushes with our hands, neare two hogsheads full of Birds in three or foure houres'*. They also called in at the Virgin Isles where they found a *'loathsome beast like a Crocodil, called a Gwayn'*. Your guess is as good as mine!

On 10th April they set off on the final leg of their journey, but on the 21st ran into violent storms. They were already three days beyond when they had calculated they should have sighted land and John Ratcliffe, Captain of the poor little Discovery, was all for turning back home, but the storm in fact blew them in the right direction and five days later George Percy recorded in his diary that *'About four o'clock in the morning we descried the land of Virginia'*.

The sight that greeted them made up for all the hardships of the voyage. It was spring and the land was ablaze with honeysuckle and wild roses. Grapes, raspberries and strawberries grew so thickly on the ground that you couldn't avoid stepping on them. There were strange trees – snake-wood and chinquapin as well as the cedar and sassafras Gosnold had taken back from his first voyage. There was an abundance of game in the woods as the Indians did most of their hunting in the winter when the fur was thick. As well as familiar animals there were opossum and raccoon which most of them had never seen before and brilliantly coloured birds, including wild turkeys, soon to be added to their diet.

Having recovered from their voyage and marvelled at the landscape, the sealed box was opened. Seven of the thirteen councillors were named; the three Captains, Gosnold, Newport and Ratcliffe, Gosnold's kinsman Edward

Maria Wingfield, experienced mariners George Kendall and John Martin, and an unruly soldier of fortune named John Smith who had grumbled so much about the conditions on the voyage that Captain Gosnold had clapped him in irons!

The council members, in accordance with their instructions, elected a president for the first year, choosing Wingfield, presumably because he had the largest financial stake in the Company. Next they had to choose a site for their settlement and a party set out to explore further inland. They returned with reports of a huge river stretching far into the interior so the settlers prepared to move on. Before they set sail they held a service to give thanks to God and erected a cross on the headland which they called Cape Henry in honour of King James' eldest son. The river they named the James River in honour of the King himself. At one point they clashed with an Indian hunting party and several of the settlers were wounded including Gabriel Archer, who was secretary of the Council and who had sailed with Gosnold and documented his previous expedition. But on the whole the aboriginal Indians they met as they explored the river banks were friendly and entertained them in their villages with banquets and dancing.

By 13th May they had travelled some 30 miles upriver and thought they had found what they were looking for. It was a flat peninsula, some 3 miles long, varying between 300 and 2,000 yards wide, on the north bank of the river. Its only connection to the mainland was a narrow strip of land which was covered at high tide, making it easy to defend, but on the river side there was deep water, making a safe anchorage for the ships. Fear of attack by the Spaniards made the safety of the site paramount and overode the disadvantages of the low lying, poor boggy soil and the mosquitoes which bred in the swamps. Bartholomew Gosnold was almost alone in declaring it unsuitable and was overruled by the rest of the Council.

On 14th May the Council and the colonists all went ashore and formally named the site Jamestown. John Smith had now, at the request of Captain Newport, been released from his imprisonment and he set about organising the settlers into a workforce to build a log fort. Many of them had never done a day's work in their lives but he drove them on at a furious pace, fearing another attack. His fears were justified when, with the fort only half finished, the settlement was attacked by hostile Indians who killed one boy and wounded eleven men before being driven off by a shot from the ship's gun. Only then did President Wingfield agree to the fort having a palisade with guns at each corner and to the men being armed.

The Indians who lived in the surrounding area were governed by a powerful warrior chief named Powhatan. These tribes still lived a stone-age existence. They had no metal, had not discovered the wheel and lived in grass huts in clearings near streams, cultivating corn, squashes, beans and tobacco. The men hunted in winter and fished the streams with spears from dugout canoes or collected shellfish from the waters along the shore. The tribes frequently fought each other and were experts at surprise attack and ambush. They were dangerous enemies for they neither showed nor expected mercy.

As well as repulsing Indian attacks the settlers had many other problems to contend with. The water supply, even so far up-river, was salty and the mosquitoes were of the deadly malaria-bearing variety. Despite this the colonists persevered. They completed the fort and mounted the ships' canons on the bulwarks, cut down trees to make clearings for their tents and loaded the timber onto the ships, made gardens to grow vegetables and nets to catch fish. Within the acre enclosed by the walls of the fort they built simple homes and a church. On 14th May they had stretched a piece of sailcloth between two trees, erected an altar and Robert Hunt, who had been so near death at the beginning of the voyage, had celebrated communion according to the rites of the English Church for the first time in an overseas colony.

While all this activity was going on Captain Newport had led a small party of settlers further up the river, obeying the instructions of the Company to look for a Northwest Passage. At some falls about 50 miles from Jamestown they found a fair-haired child living in an Indian village. It was thought he might be the son of a survivor from Raleigh's lost colony. They had also made contact with the fearsome Chief Powhatan, who had greeted them cordially and feasted them royally, but they returned to Jamestown having discovered no indication that there was a way through the continent to the South Seas.

On 22nd June 1607 Captain Christopher Newport set sail for England to collect more supplies. He took with him some stones veined with a glittering metallic substance which he hoped might be gold, cedarwood logs and sassafras roots, leaving the settlers with provisions for about three months, by which time he hoped to return. Before long they were in deep trouble. They found it impossible to work in the heat and humidity and the brackish water, rotting food and inadequate sanitation caused an outbreak of dysentery. Most terrible of all was the malaria.

Weak from illness, miserable and irritable, the Council members began to quarrel. Petty arguments escalated into major disputes and Captain Newport's diplomacy and calming influence were sorely missed. The colonists began to die by the dozen and one of the victims was Captain Bartholomew Gosnold. He died of 'swamp fever', otherwise malaria, on 22nd August 1607 and was *'honourably buried with a gun salute from the fortress'*. The Council was reduced to five but even then they couldn't agree and Wingfield, his kinsman dead, was overthrown by an alliance between John Smith, Captain Ratcliffe and the mariner John Martin. They accused Wingfield of allotting food unfairly, of being an atheist and of being a Spanish spy! Captain Ratcliffe was elected president and the conspirators soon found a way of getting rid of Kendall as well, accusing him of plotting a mutiny and executing him out of hand.

By December of 1607 the colonists seemed doomed. Their food was running low, there was no sign of Captain Newport and they were constantly threatened by the Indians. It was now that the mutinous John Smith came into his own. He left Jamestown to try to obtain provisions from the Indians but was captured by Powhatan and his comrades killed, giving rise to the legend of his release after the intercession of Princess Pocohontas. Whatever the truth of the matter, by the time Newport returned in January 1608 there were only between thirty and forty of the original one hundred and forty settlers still alive. The reprieved Captain Smith set about instituting a compulsory workforce with the emphasis on self-sustaining agriculture. He introduced maize as a crop and in September of that year was elected President of the Council. In 1609 a new Charter was granted, vesting control of the colony in a Council selected by the Company and extending the colony's boundaries north and south from Old Point Comfort 200 miles in each direction and *'from sea to sea'*.

It is sad that Bartholomew did not live to see the success of the settlement he had worked so hard to set up and that he isn't given due recognition for his work. He was, for example, the first man to plant wheat in America. He was described by a contemporary as *'a man of merit, worthy of perpetual memory'*.

An interesting aside is the fact that the 3rd Earl of Southampton, Gosnold's friend and sponsor, also sponsored William Shakespeare and it is not beyond the bounds of possibility that Bartholomew Gosnold and Shakespeare met. The bard certainly had access to the Journal kept during Gosnold's 1602 voyage by Archer and Brereton and some of the wording in *The Tempest* is almost identical to sections of that Journal. He may even have based his island on a description of Cuttyhunk! By coincidence some 300 years later when I was a pupil at Hymers College I appeared in a school production of the Tempest playing Ariel. Spooky!

CHILDHOOD

In which we encounter the Little Red Bike and the first stirrings of an interest in medicine as I grew up in Hornsea, losing a father and acquiring a stepfather in a remarkably short space of time.

My own personal memories of the Gosnolds begin with my grandparents who lived in Hornsea, a small town on the East coast of Yorkshire. They had retired there in 1944 from a small terraced house in De La Pole Avenue in Hull where my grandmother had given birth to ten sons and two daughters. Rumour has it that one day a gypsy called at the house and when my grandmother declined to buy any of her wares the gypsy retreated down the path, cursing loudly, and prophesying that my grandmother would never rear a female child. Both daughters died before their third birthdays but all ten sons thrived and were the scourge of the neighbourhood. A Mrs Phillips who lived next door had vivid memories of the family, giving rise to a strange coincidence many years later when my first wife and I went to live on Anlaby Road in Hull. Soon after we moved in our neighbour called to me over the fence. 'Is your name Gosnold?' I admitted that it was. 'So how many children do *you* have?' she asked, somewhat belligerently I thought. She turned out to be the same Mrs Phillips who had lived next door to my grandparents so many years before! She was the perfect neighbour and became a great friend.

My grandfather, George Gosnold, born in Hoddesdon, Hertfordshire in 1874, ran away from home when he was 16 and joined the army. He went to Hong Kong in 1897 and subsequently took part in the Boxer Rising in China. My grandmother, Edith Jane Thomas, was born in Aberdeen in 1883, the daughter of a Sergeant Major, and went to live in Hong Kong at the age of 2. My grandparents met at a Christian Endeavour Garden Party, became engaged in 1899 and were married in Hong Kong in 1900, a few months before the Boxer Rising. They returned to the UK in 1902 and lived in New Southgate in London with George's parents, where my father was born later that same year. From there they moved to Glasgow, then on to Barry in South Wales before moving to Hull in 1910.

During the First World War my grandfather served with the Royal Garrison of Artillery in France, where he was awarded the Military Cross. In 1916 he returned to Hull to form a new regiment, recruiting a variety of people including policemen and bus drivers. Unfortunately just before his death he burned all his personal papers and diaries without allowing anyone to read them, so many of the details of his undoubtedly interesting life went with him to the grave.

By the time I knew my grandparents they had moved to Strawberry Gardens in Hornsea some 25 miles north-east of the port of Hull. The bungalow, an old semi-detached cottage, was filled with relics from his army days including, amongst the spice jars and oriental ornaments, the pigtail of a Chinaman who had attacked him in an alleyway in Shanghai and whom he had killed in self-defence, cutting off his pigtail as a souvenir. There were beautiful porcelain dishes and the air was permanently scented by exotic perfumes emanating from the many oriental momentos. Grandfather, a distinguished looking man with white hair, always seemed to be creosoting sheds and fences and the smell of creosote and of the jam grandmother used to make from the wild strawberries also evoke vivid childhood memories of Strawberry Gardens. I loved to 'escape' to their house.

The middle years of the Second World War must have been very distressing for my grandparents, as they were for so many families. Their eldest son, George, my father, died of tuberculosis just before Christmas 1943, aged 41. Their second youngest, Len, was blown up by a mine in Italy, although thankfully not fatally injured. Then Peter, their youngest, was shot down and killed while returning from a bombing raid in November 1944. He had joined the RAF in 1943. Despite being rejected initially as unsuitable for aircrew he reapplied and was accepted for training as a Flight Engineer. He was posted to 514 Squadron, stationed at Waterbeach in Cambridgeshire, flying operations in Lancaster bombers. He had completed his tour of thirty operations and was due for a break but volunteered to stand in for his best friend, who was getting married. As so often seems to happen it was one operation too many. On 21st November 1944, 514 Squadron was part of a fleet of 160 planes which mounted an all-out daylight assault on a German oil refinery in Hamburg, a target which had survived several previous raids. The operation was a complete success and only three planes failed to return, all of them Lancasters, all from 514 Squadron. Peter's aircraft was hit over Germany but managed to limp over the border into Holland, where it crash-landed. The pilot and navigator survived and were taken prisoner but Peter and the other four crew members all died. Peter was just 20 years old. In 1950 my grandparents celebrated their Golden Wedding but my grandfather died the following year when I was nine. My grandmother lived on for another thirteen years during which time I visited her often to top up on those evocative smells.

I was born on 10th March 1942 at Sunnybrae, Belgrave Drive in Hornsea, the youngest of three children, little brother to Thelma and Tony. I was christened John Kenelm Gosnold. I have never really known why 'Kenelm', except that there was a Yorkshire landowner called Sir Kenelm Caley. I know that my mother knew of him but whether she admired him from afar or just liked the name I have been unable to find out. There may of course be another explanation altogether.

My father, George Lionel Gosnold, was the eldest of the ten boys who lived in De La Pole Avenue and had to help to bring up his brothers. He went to Nottingham University where he trained as an industrial chemist, subsequently taking a Teaching Certificate as an external graduate. My mother, Florence Edna Wilson, was born and grew up in the village of Eastwood in Nottinghamshire, birthplace of D H Lawrence, who reputedly used to take her for walks when she was a small girl. Eventually the Wilsons moved north to Hull to run a hosiery and wool shop in Gypsyville, then a pleasant residential suburb in East Hull. My mother paid her own way through Art School in Leeds. By day she was learning photography, by night earning money by playing the piano in the city's clubs. My parents met in Hull and married there in 1927. They lived at first with my mother's parents, moved to Nottingham while my father was at University and finally to Sunnybrae in Hornsea in 1932.

After teaching for several years at Francis Askew School in Hull my father eventually became Headmaster of Brunswick Avenue School in the same city. I still meet former pupils of both establishments who remember him with affection and always have a good word to say about him. He contracted tuberculosis and was too ill to be called up for active service in World War II but as a member of Toc H he was responsible for evacuating children from the beleaguered city of Hull with its frequent heavy bombing raids to the relative safety of North Lincolnshire, but eventually he became too ill even for that. I have no clear personal memories of him as he died in December 1943 when I was almost two and he spent much of that time ill in bed (some of it in a chicken shed at the bottom of our garden at Sunnybrae) or in the local sanatorium at Castle Hill Hospital. I do vaguely remember my mother making frequent trips to the shed with trays of soup and tea but little else apart from the day of his funeral, which I wasn't allowed to attend. That day appears very clear in my memory, although more likely in view of my age, to have been remembered from story rather than actual experience. I was clearly deeply affected at being excluded from the family occasion and can remember as though it was yesterday the closing of the front door at Sunnybrae, leaving me behind. Since then opening and closing doors have become symbolic of my life, dividing it into compartments, all quite separate from each other.

My mother was a strange lady – bizarre even – a manic depressive, but a very talented artist. I have several of her paintings displayed on my walls and am happy to have inherited a little of her interest in art. You could always tell her mood from her paintings – dark and sombre when she was feeling low but very much more precise and cheerful when she was on a high. She was a very determined character and decided from the beginning that I was going to be a success in life – preferably in the teaching profession like my father. She had two mottoes by which she lived and which she passed on to me, one on the side of a pencil case, 'Work hard and play hard', and the other 'Be good and let who will be clever'.

Sunnybrae was a pleasant bungalow with three bedrooms, two reception rooms and a lean-to kitchen. Although we moved from it soon after my father died I remember it well as we subsequently moved back there after a break of two years. It was from Sunnybrae when I was only 3 years old that I set out on my great adventure on my Little Red Bike, again a symbolic pre-empting of my life and career, an example of the determination and willfulness inherited from my mother and the fascination that exploration of the unknown held for my ancestors.

My mother was always buying things she couldn't afford, extravagant presents for birthdays and Christmas, one of which was 'The Little Red Bike' – a bright red tricycle with big handlebars and large rear wheels with solid tyres. I loved that bike! I soon mastered the art of pedalling and pottered around the garden for hours. I progressed to the pavement outside the house but was, like the mother of 'James James Morrison Morrison' in the childhood rhyme, told that I 'must NEVER go down to the end of the town'. Of course, like James James Morrison's mother, I took no notice, seeing no danger, and one day when my mother was busy I set off to explore. Fortunately in 1945 there were very few cars on the road. Car owners were not common and the few that there were were either away fighting or their cars were laid up for the duration.

I set off down Belgrave Drive, onto Hall Road, across Cliff Road – now a very busy main road – into Hartley Street, past the Floral Hall, turned right along the Promenade, successfully negotiated the forecourt of the Marine Hotel and disappeared along Marine Drive. Not of course that the names meant anything to me at the time, but I had apparently chatted to several people along the way, none of whom seemed to think it strange that I was on my own. I ended up on the South Promenade by the Boating Lake, in those days a beautiful and extensive stretch of water with a large building by it.

From there I made my way to the Fire Station in Burton Road. Fire-engines always held a strong fascination for me. Mother had noticed that I was missing shortly after I left and panicked totally. Eventually, after a frantic search in the immediate vicinity she called the Police. It took them half a day to find me. Sergeant Tiplady spotted me near the Fire Station and I was returned to my demented mother, to receive the first tanning of my young life. Even worse, my beloved bike was confiscated for two weeks, a far more painful punishment. It didn't change things however, I still used to head off into the unknown at every opportunity and have remained stubborn, hot-headed, impulsive and obstinate to this day. Since those early childhood escapades, if I have wanted to do something, by and large I have done it and hang the consequences. It has caused problems throughout my life, although I hope age has tempered all these qualities to a certain extent. They have also, I must confess, been assets in many aspects of my life and career.

In 1945, despite rumours that she was involved with our widowed family doctor, my mother married the local milkman, James Hartley, whose first wife, Clarice, had been killed in a road accident in February 1940. She had set out from Hornsea in the evening on her bicycle to visit her parents at Cowden, a village a few miles further along the coast, her bicycle lights blacked out in accordance with wartime regulations. There had been a prolonged period of ice and snow but it seemed to have eased. However as darkness fell the rutted snow began to freeze again. No-one knows exactly what happened but she was found by the driver of a bus lying in the road unconscious, still astride her bicycle. He took her to Hornsea Hospital where she died a week later as a result of a fractured skull.

When my mother and Jim married Sunnybrae was let and we all moved to Jim's small house in Rolston, a hamlet on the coast three miles south of Hornsea. My stepfather had two sons, Brian, who was 13, and David, 11, and by that time my sister Hazel had been born – quite a houseful. At my mother's insistence Brian and David were sent to live with 'Aunty Ida', Clarice's sister, on her farm in Burstwick, a village a few miles inland. Ida had given up her job when her sister was killed and moved to Rolston to look after her brother-in-law and nephews. She stayed with them throughout the war, then left to marry Burstwick farmer Eric Speight. I only got to know Ida well in later years when I was her family doctor. Thelma, who was just 13, and Tony, 7, had been evacuated to Ripley in Derbyshire during the war and were now boarders at Josiah Masons School in Erdington, a suburb of Birmingham. They only rarely visited home, so I was to all intents and purposes brought up as an only child until the birth of my half-sister Hazel. (I say half-sister but

Thelma has always insisted that Hazel was our father's child.) This splitting up of the family sowed the seeds for the sad disputes that swept through it in later life.

I do remember going with my mother once to visit Thelma and Tony in Erdington. The school had been founded by Josiah Masons and was a charitable organisation run by the National Association of Schoolmasters for the children of teachers who had died. We stayed in a boarding house in Erdington. I wasn't very old and was left behind to be looked after by the landlady while mother went to the school. I was in the bedroom playing and crawled inside the large wardrobe which, being unsteady, toppled forward when I leaned against the front, closing the door and trapping me inside as it fell against the bed. I shouted and shouted but nobody heard me and I was locked in for a long time until found by my distressed mother.

The house at Rolston had no hot water or indoor lavatory and there was only linoleum on the bedroom floors. My mother was fairly strict but I learned to get around her quite well. She was very prim and due to the lack of hot water on tap family ablutions were performed in the living room in front of the AGA. Mother would undress and dress under a large dressing-gown and a towel, never exposing herself to any other member of the family. In 1946 we moved back to Sunnybrae but I still went to Rolston every morning with Jim before going to school.

My education began at the Mereside School in Hornsea, a small school with only two classes. There was a slight hiccup during my second term when the infamous snows of 1947 began to fall on my fifth birthday, 10th March. So that people could get out somebody dug a path along Belgrave Drive with narrow channels to each house, the snow on either side being well above my head. Mereside School, as its name suggests, was adjacent to Hornsea Mere, an extensive stretch of fresh water only a few hundred yards inland from the sea. There were no male teachers at the school. The Headmistress was a Mrs Parrot who boxed my ears when, egged on by my friends, I stood outside the door of her study chanting 'Pretty Polly, Pretty Polly, Pretty Polly'.

I remember Empire Days when we dressed up in colonial national costumes and brought in boxes of South African apples and donations to the Empire Fund. One year I was dressed up as a Red Indian and danced around a wigwam. I was escorted to school by my mother who wheeled Hazel perched on her famous bicycle which she then rode home. I of course had to walk, despite pleading to be allowed to go on the Little Red Bike, to which I was still very attached. At lunchtimes we had to take our packed lunches and march in a crocodile to the Congregational Church Hall, some 400 yards away, to eat. I had become friendly with a girl called Gerina Davies and always walked with her which led to a great deal of teasing from our schoolfellows. Even at that age I had an eye for the girls.

We never went away on holiday as a family when I was young but I was sent on Methodist holidays along with a boy called Paul Owen, who now lives opposite me in Lelley. One occasion I remember particularly well was spent in a girls' school in Shropshire called Moreton Hall – a beautiful place set in acres of gardens and spreading lawns. The dormitories were on the top floor of the house and one night we boys went exploring in the loft, accessed through a door in our dormitory. We crawled along for what seemed ages, then somebody fell through a gap between the rafters, landing on one of the girl's beds and leading to questions being asked in the house!

Twice I went to Anglesey, camping in a place called Benllech Bay. I have happy memories of comradeship and of learning new games like 'puddocks', a kind of non-stop cricket played with a big ball, beach hockey which inflicted terrible bruises to the ankles, and of enjoying all sorts of outdoor activities. A highlight of these holidays was the train trip over the Menai suspension bridge to Llanfairpwyithgwyndrobwilgaigergeryphlantisilogogogoch – I think!

One not so good memory of those days is of when John Blades and I camped at Mappleton on Neville Lofthouse's farm and went down with food poisoning. We had been attracted there by the prospect of being allowed to drive a tractor, to try our hand at ploughing and for John to cement his relationship with Jane, Neville's younger sister. We were rescued by our parents after three days of vomiting and diarrhoea, by which time we were really quite ill and severely dehydrated.

One of the reasons for not having family holidays was of course my stepfather's milkround. In a morning before going to school I had to help with the horse which pulled the cart and with the filling of the wide-topped bottles and putting on the cardboard tops. The cart was then loaded up with crates of bottles which had succeeded the ten gallon churns, whose contents used to be ladled into jugs which were covered with lace doilies weighed down with coloured beads and left out on the step by householders. After school there were bottles to wash. In later years automation took over many of the jobs, the cardboard tops being replaced by foil and the horse and cart by a van.

Jim Hartley had been given the milkround by his father Bernard, who had started his working life as a butcher in Waterloo Street in Hull, made a bob or two and bought a farm in Holderness and eventually a property in the North Riding, becoming quite a wealthy man. Jim spent his childhood in Hull but when he was 15 his father decided to 'retire'. He sold his butcher's business and bought Home Farm in Rolston. To his great regret Jim had to leave school and become a 'farmhand'. His mother said she had never had to work so hard in her life! There were meals to prepare for the extra hands at haytime, harvest and threshing days and the farmhouse was old, with no electricity or modern plumbing, although Bernard did eventually have electricity installed. Despite all the hard work and wages of only ten shillings a week Jim was very happy. He bought a motorbike and led a very active social life. He had two brothers, one of whom died in Egypt, the other following his father's trade as a butcher.

Jim married Clarice Swift in 1932 and they moved to Hornsea, where, the following year, their elder son was born and Jim's father let him have the milkround he had built up in the town. Grandad Hartley retired for the second time in 1936, selling Home Farm and building himself a new house, Rosegarth, nearby. He also bought a smaller house in Rolston called Sycamores, built on a dairy, stables and garage and let it to Jim and Clarice for ten shillings a week, and it was there that their second son was born. At the same time Jim changed over from delivering their own milk straight from the churns and started collecting it from local farmers and bottling it in the dairy at Rolston, entailing, he maintained, 'a lot more work and not much profit'. He was delighted when, many years later, compulsory pasteurisation regulations forced him to buy his milk wholesale, ready bottled. Throughout the war he served as a part-time fireman, spending one night a week sleeping at the fire station and the rest of the time 'on call'.

In the early days, when the milk was still being taken out in the horse-drawn cart, the bottles were sometimes left in the outside toilets to keep cool. Some of these privies were double-seaters. I remember one in particular at No 1 Burton Road, which had two kinds of loo-paper hung on strings on either side - the Telegraph on one, the Daily Mirror on the other. The milkround started very early in the morning with the local cottages in Rolston, then down Rolston Road, round New Estate, up and down Hull Road and into Southgate Gardens by about 9.00am, where a Mrs Stephenson provided breakfast. She had two sons, David and John, (the latter now retired from his post as Superintendent in the Humberside Police Force). Her husband worked as a general labourer, gardener and mortuary attendant at the Hornsea Cottage Hospital and we were to meet again in very different circumstances many years later. He left for work long before Jim arrived. If I was accompanying my stepfather I was rarely allowed in as I had to look after the horse, giving it its nosebag and finding it a drink of water. Jim always emerged looking well satisfied, presumably the result of a good breakfast!

As the business expanded a bicycle was used for deliveries as well as the pony and trap, and then a van which was driven by Jim. This left Jim's assistant Albert to drive the horse and cart on his own while Stan, his other employee, took the bicycle. They were both quite mad. On Christmas Eve they would set off as usual at about 6.30am, Albert driving the horse and Stan on the bicycle. They were plied with drinks and generous tips almost from the moment they started until they completed the round at about 2 o'clock in the afternoon at the top of Cliff Road in Hornsea. The road is level from Atwick Gap to the top of the bus station, drops downhill to another flat stretch, then down again to the crossroads at the bottom of Eastgate. Residents in the area used to look forward all year to the sight of Albert with the horse and cart full of empty milkbottles and Stan on his bicycle, both completely legless, gathering pace as they raced down the hills. A highly dangerous pastime which as far as I can remember never led to either accident or arrest.

However I can remember once when they had been for a night out together and were involved in a car accident at Lissett Crossroads, as a result of which they both sustained quite serious injuries. Stan was off work for a month, Albert for two and I had to take the last two weeks of the summer term off school and work right through the holidays to help to keep the business going. I was, I think, fourteen or fifteen at the time. On the whole I enjoyed living and working in the country, going out on the haycart, helping with the harvest, stooking corn, going after rabbits, cheese sandwiches for lunch – and ploughing in cold weather! They were good times, they are good memories.

Not so good are my vague memories of the war, rather hazy as I was only three and a half when it ended, so some of it must be hearsay. After the raids on Hull with its strategically important docks the German bombers used to fly over Hornsea on their way home and release any bombs they had left. One of these hit the electricity sub-station which was only about 200 yards from our bungalow. The blast blew in the windows and showered my cot with glass. Mother, running through the house to see if I was all right, fell and broke her ankle. Apparently I slept through the whole performance. Next morning the chickens from next door's henhouse were seen hanging roasted in the trees.

The first van my stepfather bought was a Ford, registration number FWF 551, on the side of which was the legend *'James Hartley, Dairyman, Rolston, near Hornsea'*. Once when I was about nine we went in the Ford van on a two-day trip to London. It is difficult to appreciate now what an adventure that was. It was 1951 – the year of the Festival of Britain – and we went exploring the Big City. The traffic was not nearly as dense as it is now of course, but as we turned into The Mall heading for Buckingham Palace we were stopped by a policeman. He stuck his head in the window looking totally bewildered. "Rolston. Where's Rolston?" he asked. The only 'Hornsea' he knew was Hornsey in north-east London. It turned out that the reason he had stopped us was because commercial vehicles were not allowed in The Mall and we were quickly escorted away lest we should offend their Majesties!

By the time the Ford had been replaced by an Austin, PWF 41, I was heavily into model plane making. There was to be a competition at Hymers College in Hull where I was now at school and I had spent months making a detailed model. The working van had just two seats up front so an old car seat was put loose in the back for when there was more than one passenger. We placed the plane carefully on the floor behind this seat and set off. Driving through the village of Ellerby we had to brake sharply, the unsecured seat rolled forward then shot backwards, crushing my plane. I was absolutely heartbroken.

Two members of my 'extended' family I remember well are 'Aunty' Phoebe Lonsdale and 'Aunty' Ethel. Aunty Phoebe, a friend of my mother and Thelma's Godmother, was a huge lady weighing sixteen or seventeen stones with a thin husband who I think was an accountant. They had three children, Martin, Neville and Elspeth. We were quite friendly with them and I used to go and stay with them sometimes at weekends. Auntie Phoebe was famous for her Yorkshire puddings. They were tremendous, served as a starter with delicious gravy, as part of the main course or as a sweet with either butter and sugar, syrup, or sugar and lemon.

Despite the fact that I had been christened in St Nicholas' Church in Hornsea, which was C of E, Auntie Phoebe used to take me to Hornsea Methodist Chapel on Sunday mornings and I became a member of the Methodist Youth Club. My introduction to drama was a stage show put on in the Methodist Church Hall when I had to sing a solo. I was so frightened that to my intense embarrassment I wet myself, but fortunately nobody seemed to notice the wet patch on the floor where I had been standing.

When I was about 8 or 9 years old I joined the St Nicholas Church choir and was chosen to make the traditional start to the Christmas Eve Carol Service by singing the first verse of 'Once in Royal David's City' from the back of the church, unaccompanied and in the dark. I was given the note in the vestry but by the time I had scampered round the outside of the church to the main door, hitting that first note correctly was a bit of a lottery and I resorted to a tuning fork struck on a gravestone before I entered the church! After a while I became an Altar Server and subsequently Head Server until one fateful Christmas Day when I was 18. I had over-indulged on Hull

Brewery ale in the Rose and Crown the previous evening and mixed up the jugs of water and wine after the Communion. The Vicar was not amused when I poured wine over his hands and said so fairly forcibly afterwards. It was the final straw for my already sceptical view of religion. Whatever happened to Christian forgiveness, especially on Christmas Day? When I went to St Thomas' Hospital in London I was, however, able to continue my singing with the London University Choir who sang in the church in Langham Place, next to Broadcasting House.

Aunty Ethel was married to my maternal grandfather, Mr Wilson, who was verger at the Methodist Chapel in Hessle, a village to the west of Hull. They lived in a small side-street off Hull Road in Hessle and I used to visit them regularly. Aunty Ethel was an extremely good cook and made wonderful cakes, especially little butterfly buns, as light as a feather. An overiding memory is of Grandad Wilson listening to the Archers religiously every evening and everyone having to keep absolutely silent for fifteen minutes. If anyone coughed or shuffled he would get very cross.

When Grandad Wilson died Aunty Ethel remarried, a very wealthy man, who was already quite ill and died soon after. She was on her own again. By then my mother was very ill and Aunty Ethel helped my stepfather to look after Hazel and me, although I was about to go to University. Mother was in and out of Broadgates Hospital near Beverley, being treated for depression. She became more and more ill, eventually having to have a mastectomy for breast cancer. Aunty Ethel moved in with my stepfather whenever my mother was in hospital, an arrangement which seemed to suit him very well! By then Sunnybrae had been sold and Jim had bought Whiteways in Strawberry Gardens, very close to the house where Grandma Gosnold had lived. Just before my mother's death in 1979, aged 78, when I was married and living on Anlaby Road in Hull, she came to live with us for a while. During those long years of her illness a great deal of bitterness and resentment had built up in the family.

After her death James Hartley married Aunty Ethel which, as she had at one time been married to my mother's father, meant that technically he married his step-mother-in-law! No wonder he was known as 'Lucky Jim'! I remember reluctantly going to St Nicholas' Church for the ceremony and asking the vicar why the Church of England allowed someone to marry their step-mother-in-law. His only answer was that at their age they were quite safe! I have always had mixed feelings about Aunty Ethel. There are good memories but in some ways she was responsible for rifts in the family. After she died Jim, at the age of 84, moved in with Mrs Stephenson who used to

33

provide him with breakfast all those years ago on the milkround. He died in 1994, aged 87. He was always a bit of a lad and clearly was unable to exist without some female company. Another family trait?!

Tony, my elder brother, returned home from Birmingham when he finished school and went on to Art College in Hull. I think he resented the fact that I hadn't been sent away to school and there were often quite bitter rows. He scoffed at my 'posh public school' and life at home became very difficult. After two years at the College of Art he started work at the now famous Hornsea Pottery which in those days operated from a little house in Victoria Avenue off The Esplanade. It was founded by the two Rawson brothers, Malcolm and Desmond, and John Clappison. As the business expanded it moved to Old Hall in the Market Place. More kilns were bought and it started to do very well. They were a good team. John Clappison, a talented artist, and Tony with his artistic temperament complemented the Rawsons' business acumen and the company developed rapidly. Tony however couldn't cope with the heat from the kilns. He had severe Athlete's Foot, a fungal infection the smell of which I can still remember (yet another evocative smell for me) and he left to join the Royal Navy. After eleven years he married and quit the service, going into the Police Force in Stockport, near Manchester, which was his wife Pauline's home. He was doing well and enjoying it until he was transferred to the CID which meant being away from home quite a lot. He gave up that job as well, and by now seemed to have a real problem settling permanently into any regular employment.

By this time our stepfather, Jim Hartley, was ready to retire and offered Tony the milkround in Hornsea. It was a total disaster. Tony thought Jim was giving him the business but Jim expected to be paid. There were immense family rows with Jim eventually threatening legal proceedings and involving a solicitor. It was the final rift in the fragmented family. Tony packed it in and went into road haulage, leaving relationships which are still strained between us even after all these years.

I have, however, always got on well with Thelma. She has always been available for advice and her home has been a haven to run to in times of trouble. When she left school she came home to Sunnybrae for about eighteen months, sharing a bedroom with Hazel. She had a good job with Northern Dairies in Hull but on one of her days off, without telling anybody she travelled to Newcastle and joined the WRENS. She left when she married Maurice, a Captain in the Fleet Air Arm who subsequently joined British Airways and is now retired. They have four children, Karen, Simon, Mandy and Robin. Karen was in fact born at Sunnybrae in Hornsea, where Thelma sometimes stayed when Maurice was at sea. Strangely enough, Thelma was the first baby Dr French delivered as a Family Practitioner in Hornsea, and Karen was the last! I can remember holding Karen soon after she was born, being fascinated by her size and total dependency and then developing an increasing interest in the welfare of babies and children, which has strongly influenced my medical career to this day. Thelma and Maurice now live in the Lake District with their family nearby, unstinting in their friendship and support, especially in recent years when my domestic life has sometimes been in turmoil. We visit occasionally and have developed a real love for the area.

Hazel was also born at Sunnybrae, in June 1944. She went first to the Mereside School then to Bridlington High School for Girls. After training at an Occupational Therapy school in Derby she met Ron and, much to Jim's distress, emigrated with him to Africa. They had three sons and she and Ron worked in a nursery growing crops on the banks of Lake Tanganyika in Zambia. Ron, an ex-submariner, also developed a fish transport business, delivering fish from Mbala to Lusaka. Tragically Hazel was murdered by drunken terrorists in front of her husband and sons in February 1981 and Ron was left to bring up the boys. As a result he developed a drink problem, often leaving the boys in the care of a nanny or even to their own devices, and died in Zambia in the mid 1990s. Their eldest son, Shannon, remained in Zambia while the second son, Cimmeron, now lives in London. The youngest, Alaric, died from malaria while still a child, a sad link with his explorer ancestor Bartholomew.

That then is my family. Some of them will crop up from time to time in the rest of this story and you will certainly recognise them when they do as those early days have had a strong influence on the rest of my life.

My grandparents, George and Edith in a lovely 'pose of rest' taken in their younger and fitter years. July 1930.

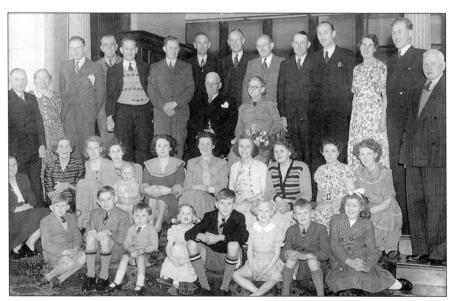

The Golden Wedding, with all remaining family present, in 1950.

A family photo in 1943 - both grandfather and father very poorly. Mother pregnant?

Me, age 7 months. Clearly a happy baby!

Father

Mother

*A pair - around the time of
their marriage in 1927.*

Dad with Thelma, on her 'little bike',
and Tony as a new baby.

Dad with the Francis Askew football team around 1927, so much like my friend
David Stevenson 60 years later.

An 'unhappy' mother with her new husband, Jim, with the four of us around 1946. Her comments on the back of the photo... "I like John on this one and Hazel, but the rest are awful"

A 'happier' mother with just the four children, around 1946.

Was this the back door to the house in Rolston, where I lived for two years after my mother married the milkman?

A later group photo with Thelma missing, showing the first milk van... The Ford, registration FWF 551, around 1948.

Another well-known face around the streets of Hornsea. Jim Hartley, who delivered milk twice daily for most of his working life. He is seen here as a young man with his carrier bike. This was in the days when milk came in churns and was ladled out in half or one pint amounts into the customer's milk jug.

Jim Hartley delivering milk in his horse drawn milk float in Southgate. He was a familiar sight in the town from the 1930's when this photograph was taken well into the 1970's. By that time bottles, sterilsation and refrigeration had taken over from the horse drawn float and the milk churn.

The South East Yorkshire Light and Power Company building destroyed in 1942, when I was aged 5 months, showering me with glass as the bedroom window of Sunnybrae was blown in. Mother, dashing through to rescue me, fell and sprained her ankle. (Reproduced with the kind permission of Dr Walker and, especially, the Hornsea Museum)

"Guess who", - yes me, - on the beach at Hornsea with bucket and spade, the weather rather inclement and the rest of the beach deserted!

43

Was I bored! A photograph taken of me with a fit looking mother around 1949.

or

Was I upset! A portrait taken about 1947.

Hazel

A rather good looking Medical Student in 1963, taken for my 21st birthday and my passport for an impending trip to play rugby in Germany.

SCHOOLDAYS

Ten years at Hymers College in Hull, shot through with my love of sport, and the forging of life-long friendships.

As I have mentioned before my mother was in many ways a strange lady. Despite her Midlands upbringing she had a strong streak of the famous Yorkshire stubbornness in her nature. Once she got an idea into her head she would not let it go and she had made up her mind that whatever else happened I was going to have 'a good education'. This, as I have said, caused problems with the rest of the family, particularly my brother Tony. She was also determined that I should not be sent away to school but stay at home where she could keep an eye on me so, at the age of 8, she entered me for the Entrance Examination to the Preparatory Department of Hymers College, a minor Public School in the nearby city of Kingston upon Hull. It had a proud tradition and was very popular, being the only 'private' school in the city apart from the Catholic Marist College. I duly passed the exam (all credit to Mereside primary school) which delighted my mother who declared there and then her intention of keeping me at that school for the next ten years.

The '11-plus' system was still in operation then and after three years in the junior school at Hymers College I duly took that exam and passed it, which entitled me to a free place and free travel from Hornsea to Bridlington Boys' Grammar School, but Mother would have none of it as I had also passed the quite separate entrance examination to Hymers College Senior School and she insisted I stayed on there. This did not, however, entitle me to free travel and it must have been difficult for my mother not only to find the daily train fare to Hull and the money for my dinners, but also to justify her decision, especially as my stepfather flatly refused to contribute towards what he considered to be an unnecessary expense. I can quite see why my brother and sisters felt put out. When it came to Hazel's turn to take the 11-plus she passed as well and went to Bridlington Girls' High School. My ten years at Hymers certainly set me aside from the rest of my family. This may have been one reason for my vulnerability to the teasing which started at primary school, carried on certainly throughout my educational years and to a certain extent throughout my life. As I grew up I learned to cope with it better and have often used it as a means of communication and teaching.

I can remember vividly the day I went to Hymers College to take the Entrance Exam. I was only just 8 years old and there were two written papers, maths and English, and an oral exam. The maths questions were already written up on the blackboard in one of the classrooms and most of them were completely foreign to me. I had no idea how to do them and I must have done very badly. The English was slightly easier. There was an actual handwriting test and a story to make up and I felt a bit better after that. Then came the oral, for which we went into the Headmaster's study. The Head in those days was a Mr Cavill, a very imposing person, but it was a pleasant interview and in due course my delighted mother was told that I had passed.

I started my ten years at Hymers College in September 1950. I travelled by train along a rural railway line similar to the one that was to play a significant part in my career much later in my life. The journeys themselves became quite an eventful part of each day, with frequent delays and breakdowns. There were several of us who travelled together regularly on the train, including Jimmy Brennand whose father was also a daily passenger. He worked as a wholesale fruiterer in Humber Street in Hull, down by the docks, a famous wholesale fruit market. He and three friends always whiled away the journey by playing solo whist. The stakes were high – old threepenny pieces, worth just over a penny in today's currency but worth quite a lot in spending power then. We used to risk getting our ears boxed by making a noise to put them off their game.

On the journey there was often a fair amount of mild bullying of we younger boys – bare knees being slapped, caps thrown out of windows and the like. The train stopped in those days at 'Botanic Gardens', a small station about a mile before the main Hull Paragon Station. Hymers College had been partially built on the site of the old Botanic Gardens. The nearest pub was called The Polar Bear, a name which puzzled visitors unfamiliar with the area. In the evening the 4.20 train also stopped at the little station to pick us up for the return journey. If we missed it we had either to walk or catch a trolley-bus into the city centre for the 5.10 or the 5.40, as these were through trains for the commuting businessmen and didn't stop at the intermediate stations. I loved the trolley-buses. They were like trams, connected to overhead power lines, but they didn't have to run on tracks. The connecting poles often came off as they negotiated the sharp bends over the railway tracks at the Botanic Crossing or at the Beverley Road corner into Ferensway near The Zoological, reputed to be one of the oldest pubs in Hull. The offices of the Hull Daily Mail now stand on that corner. Incidentally when the previous occupant of the site, Spooners' Buildings, was being demolished there was an accident one afternoon when an Irish labourer fell from the scaffolding and was fatally injured. He was still alive when he was brought into the A&E Department at

Hull Royal and was clearly very drunk after a liquid lunch and had a blood alcohol level of 300mg% – not ideal when working at heights. But I digress. If the trolleybus connectors came off they had to be hoisted back into position by the conductor with the aid of a long wooden pole. This caused even more traffic chaos at a busy junction where there were frequent hold-ups as the level crossing gates further along the road were closed for passing trains. Hull was notorious for the number of its level crossings, the problem not being alleviated until some of the lines were closed and a couple of flyovers built on the two busiest main roads.

Wednesday and Saturday afternoons were set aside for sport. If you weren't involved in any of the school teams you could go home at lunchtime on a Wednesday. The downside was that Saturday morning was a normal school day. One Wednesday lunchtime when, as luck would have it, I was travelling home alone, a woman got into my compartment with a baby. In those days most trains had separate compartments with a door at each side and not even a connecting corridor, never mind the open-plan carriages we have today. Soon after she got in she began breast-feeding the baby. I had never seen this before and whilst fascinated I was also totally embarrassed and didn't know where to look. It was in such sharp contrast to my experience of my mother who, as I have already mentioned, was a very private person and never exposed any part of her body in front of any of the family. I certainly couldn't have discussed this incident with her. All part of my education I suppose.

I stayed at Hymers College until I was 18. I wasn't all that bright and had to work very hard to keep up, even in the B-stream. I took nine Ordinary-levels as they were then and passed eight but failed dismally in history. My history teacher for my first three years in the senior school was William Pickles, who for me was a complete disaster. He seemed to have little interest in the subject himself and didn't encourage us either by example or by his style of teaching. I achieved notoriety by getting only 1% in my mock O-level history exam which presumably was for turning up and writing my name on the paper! My best subject was Latin. I was always top of the class in Latin and got 97% in my mock. I suppose I could have gone on to study classics but the little I did do has been helpful in my medical career.

I was interested and did well in geography, probably because I got on with the geography teacher Joe Gilbanks, who also taught Rugby. In fact it was he who sparked off my life-long interest in the game. I soon got into my year team and played for every year up through the school, culminating in a place in the school 1st XV in my final year. I was also into athletics and represented the city in the Yorkshire Schools Athletic Sports in 1959 when they were held at Costello Playing Fields on Boothferry Road in Hull. In those days it had a cinder track. I was the fastest runner in the school but not quite good enough for the All England Schools Championships. Hymers had reasonably good sports facilities and I made the most of them.

Having passed my O-levels I progressed into the sixth form. The school wouldn't let pupils continue on into the sixth unless their O-level results were of a sufficiently high standard to give a reasonable chance of passing several subjects at A-level. This meant that the A-level pass rate – and the school's reputation – were consistently high! I passed General Studies, Physics, Chemistry and Biology at A-level but by then my sights were firmly fixed on a medical school, which required Zoology, so I stayed on an extra year to take it as a single subject. With most of the pressure off I thoroughly enjoyed my third year in the VIth form! There were six or seven of us and we considered ourselves to be a very select group. It included Vic Doughty and John Mullins who both became psychiatrists. (Vic has now retired and emigrated to Australia.) I am myself 'Section 12 Approved', ie a 'virtual' psychiatrist – quite a coincidence. We played a lot of 'fives', cricket and rugby and participated fully in the Cadet Force band. All in all a good year.

In fact, looking back, I enjoyed most of my school days on the whole. I joined the school choir in my first year in prep school and did quite a bit of solo singing until my voice broke. Although I continued to enjoy singing after that and as I've mentioned, joined the London University Choir, my voice was never as good as it had been. I also enjoyed acting, both at school and at home. I belonged to the Hornsea Drama Group, made famous by Brian Rix, now Lord Rix, who started his stage career in the resort where he grew up. One year we entered the Holderness Drama Festival, held at Withernsea School. Our play had a cast of only four but we won the Cup for the 'Best Play' and I won the 'Best Actor' award. The adjudicator said I should have had both cups as my fellow actors hadn't been very good but I had managed to hold the play together. Their mistakes and my attempts to correct them had apparently added greatly to the comedy element of the production. I was very proud of myself.

Another inadvertently funny performance was when my singing voice let me down. The Drama Group was run by Mrs Agar who was also a music teacher and used to put on little concerts in the Village Hall. I was given a solo to sing – Orpheus and his Lute. It was apparently the funniest rendering of that piece of music that anyone had ever heard as I was totally off key. This was comparable to my 'Once In Royal David's City' solo attempt at St

Nicholas Church which one year went horribly wrong when I started much too high and had to abandon it and start again, hence my subsequent resort to the tuning fork on the gravestone. The St Nicholas Church organist, John Boxall, was a strange man who suffered from St Vitas' Dance. One of my vivid memories of those days was of the use of amyl nitrite capsules in the vestry to revive fainting members of the congregation – a not unusual occurrence when it was considered 'not done' to have anything to eat before early communion. Allied to long spells of kneeling and standing this had its inevitable consequences.

In adolescence I had quite a few friends in Hornsea, despite being at school in Hull. In fact a couple of them who I have already mentioned went to Hymers as well - Jimmy Brennand who became a Hull solicitor and Vick Doughty. Other close friends were John Blades and Peter Senior who both went to Bridlington School. We played, fought and chased girls together and got up to all the usual things that teenage boys got up to in the 1950s. A group of about twelve of us, including a few girls, belonged to the Hornsea Tennis Club in Hallgarth Park. My Mereside School friend Gerina Davies was still around, a couple of the Rix girls and Barbara Jefferson who became a member of the old Hull Health Authority, as I write is a Town Councillor and with whom on occasions I am still in touch.

When I was 15 I met Shirley Wainwright. We became very attached to one another and spent most of our spare time together over the next three years. Shirley's father, having retired from the West Yorkshire Traction Company, was a partner in a garage business next to the little round house with the thatched roof near Seaton, a village a couple of miles inland from Hornsea. It was a thriving business and the family were very well off. Shirley was taking a Shorthand and Typing course at Pitman's College on Spring Bank in Hull, very near to Hymers, and she used to travel in on the same train, which was how we met. In the evenings and at weekends I regularly used to cycle out to her house and her mother became very fond of me. I had by then definitely decided on a medical career and I think Mrs Wainwright quite fancied the idea of her daughter marrying a doctor. Shirley wasn't at all bothered about what I was going to be. She just wanted to enjoy life and life at that time included me. As an only daughter she was a bit spoilt but as her mother was a very good cook I had no objection to being made part of the family.

I became passionately interested in cars and Shirley's father managed to find an old Austin 7 for £20 which he bought for me. From then on every spare moment was spent doing it up. I stripped it right down, cleaned up the engine, polished everything that could be polished, re-chromed it, painted it, and by the time I was 17 it and I were ready for the road. I don't remember who paid for the tax and insurance – I suppose it must have been Mr Wainwright – but I certainly appreciated the freedom it gave me. The Wainwrights were also fond of taking weekend trips and used to include me in them. We would go across to the West Riding or down into Derbyshire. I spent so much time with them that my mother accused me of moving out of Sunnybrae and into the Wainwright's home.

When I was accepted at St Thomas's it was Shirley's parents who took me down there to look for digs and after I started my course they continued to visit me, staying at the Bonnington Hotel. Sometimes Shirley would come down to London by herself and we could enjoy our friendship unchaperoned! Our relationship lasted well into my medical school years but Shirley was eventually usurped by Wendy Varley whom I met while on holiday. She was a hairdresser, the daughter of local farmer Claude Varley, but although we were fond of each other it didn't last.

Considering my rather strange family situation I can still look back on my adolescence with pleasure and satisfaction. The education my mother had so set her heart on stood me in good stead in my future career, even though it wasn't the one she had chosen for me. She would have liked me to be a teacher like my father. Sadly she didn't live long enough to find out that eventually my job was to involve quite a bit of teaching, leading in 1999 to my achieving the post of Director of Postgraduate Medical Education for Hull and East Yorkshire.

MEDICAL SCHOOL

A heady mixture of living in London and working and playing (especially Rugby) at a hitherto undreamed of level in the rarefied atmosphere of the famous St Thomas'.

Having obtained all the necessary qualifications except A-level Zoology, which I was in the process of taking, I started applying for Medical School. It is quite a complicated procedure with a fair amount of choice and as it was going to be my life for at least the next six years, I had to get it right. I finally whittled down my preferences to Manchester and the two London teaching hospitals, Guy's and St Thomas'. My first interview was at Manchester and it was disastrous. I can remember the humiliation even now as the Dean told me as I left the room that I was 'not good enough' to become a doctor at all, and certainly not at Manchester.

My next interview was at Guy's and although I wasn't accepted it did teach me a valuable lesson. When asked by one of the elderly gentleman conducting it what I had done during my summer holidays I replied with perfect truth that I had painted my mother's house. He enquired with mild interest whether I worked in oils or watercolours. When, somewhat puzzled, I replied 'Snowcem', he looked up from his papers and his eyebrows climbed up into his hair with astonishment. On the train home I reflected that perfect truth and absolute honesty were not necessarily going to get me a place in Medical School. It would obviously have been preferable to say I had spent the summer helping old ladies across the road or washing floors in an orphanage or at least on a painting holiday abroad. While outright lying was to be avoided, economy with and embellishment of the truth were to be desired. Once accepted I would cope with any consequences. Armed with this new philosophy I approached the St Thomas's interview with more confidence.

The interview was held in a much smaller, more comfortable room and started with the Secretary of the selection committee, an elderly gentleman called Crockford, asking for my name. He looked me up on his list, noted my address and said "Ah, Hornsea." I was expecting the usual southerner's reaction " ....is that the Hornsey near London?" Instead he continued "Hornsea Mere?" "Yes," I said. "Do you sail?" was his next question. "Oh yes," I answered blithely. Now (a) I had never been on Hornsea Mere in my life, (b) I couldn't swim and (c) I had a phobia about water – fully justified much later in my life as we shall see. However, this gentleman wasn't to know any of those things and it seemed a harmless enough question, unlikely to affect my future medical career. "And what kind of boat do you sail," he enquired with interest, opening up the pit in front of my unsuspecting feet. Luckily, in the pub I frequented in Hornsea there were usually a few sailing types so I blurted out the only name I could remember overhearing. "Er - Fireflies." He beamed. "Great. Just the chap we're looking for for the Boating Club." I smiled rather feebly in reply and we went on with the interview which happily was successful. I was thrilled and dismissed the boating incident from my mind, assuming he had just been trying to put me at my ease and would have forgotten all about it by the following September. Unfortunately he was one of the first people I saw when I arrived to start my course. "Ah, Gosnold," he greeted me. "Boating. Good, good." I waved and nodded non-committally. All I was interested in was rugby and I had no intention of being lured onto, into or anywhere near water.

My desire to be a doctor went back to my childhood. Dr French was a big influence – quite apart from the fact that my mother was very friendly with him, so he was around the house more than perhaps was normal for the family doctor. He took care of me during childhood illnesses, along with Nurse Hewett, the District Nurse, who lived opposite Sunnybrae. I suffered from the usual crop of childhood complaints but I remember particularly when I had earache he came to see me and prescribed penicillin tablets. I thought they were horrible. I was sleeping at that time in a single bed pushed up against the wall in what was known as the 'far' bedroom. I used to spit out the tablets as soon as my mother had left the room and stuff them down between the bed and the wall. I obviously didn't make the kind of progress expected of me, which puzzled Dr French until the routine weekly 'turn-out' of my room when the cache of discarded pills was revealed. Instead of being angry he took the time and patience to explain to me what the pills did and why it was important for me to take them. After that I was given them in a spoonful of jam. Although I was very young the episode made a lasting impression on me and I have never been a believer in the philosophy that if it tastes horrible it must be doing you good, especially with children.

Dr French played an even bigger role in my life when I had a strange illness which it was feared might be polio, of which there was a widespread epidemic at the time. This was before mass immunisation had virtually eradicated it and many victims ended up with varying degrees of paralysis. I was very poorly, feverish, a sore throat, aches and pains all over but especially in my joints. I was weak and lethargic. I would have been 8 or 9. Dr French was very worried and spent a lot of time with me. I must by then have said I would like to be a doctor and he talked a lot about medicine in general and about his student days at St Thomas's. He said that if I did decide to do medicine he would support my application to St Thomas's. Idle chat to a sick child maybe, but that kind of thing remains with an impressionable youngster.

During my illness I had a torrential nosebleed and I was tended by the lovely Nurse Hewett. She was so careful and kind and became a good friend, adding her weight to the mounting store of incidents nudging me towards a medical career. Mind you, I could have been put off for life when, at the age of 3, I had my tonsils taken out at Hornsea Cottage Hospital. I can remember to this day the horror of having a mask forced over my face and the sickening smell of chloroform (another of 'those smells'). This may have been the source of my claustrophobic fear of being under water, re-inforced by my first swimming lesson at Beverley Road Baths in Hull, when I was pushed in and told to 'get swimming'. I didn't and never have. Much later in life I had cause to regret it but that's another story. Back to the Cottage Hospital. A little girl in the bed opposite me who had also had a tonsillectomy had a secondary haemorrhage a day and a half after the operation. She vomited copious amounts of blood all over the place - a very frightening sight for anybody, never mind a 3 year old.

In those days you were kept in hospital for at least a week after a tonsils operation and one day when I was resting in the general ward my new stepfather's head appeared through the window. He said he had just popped by to say hello. Because of the milkround he couldn't visit at the 'proper' time so had decided to risk Sister's wrath and come at his convenience. Sister was, of course, incensed. She was very much in charge and even in the case of very small children visiting times were strictly adhered to. It wasn't considered good for patients to have parents fussing over them, never mind the inconvenience to the nursing staff. How very different it is today thank goodness.

Another incident I can remember which made a lasting impression on me happened when I was 11 or 12. I developed a huge boil which didn't respond to the usual home remedies of kaolin poultices or the application of a hot milk bottle. It was so painful that on my Wednesday afternoon off from Hymers my mother despatched me to the Doctor's surgery. It wasn't the familiar Dr French but a new man, a Doctor Ashforth, which made me nervous in the first place. The surgery was in Eastgate in the centre of Hornsea and off I went by myself, clutching a letter of explanation from my mother. All the other patients in the waiting room were women, not really remarkable on a

Wednesday afternoon when the men would be at work and the children at school. I did notice that some of the women were rather stout and of an odd shape. Eventually Dr Ashforth put his head round the door and barked 'next' but on seeing me he came over and in an 'army-type' voice which made me quake in my shoes asked what on earth I was doing there? Mortified at being singled out and with all the natural reticence of an 11 year-old I mumbled something about a boil needing treatment and proffered my letter. It would have been bad enough explaining in the privacy of the consulting room as the boil was in a very embarrassing place, but in a waiting room full of women I felt totally humiliated. He seemed quite oblivious, merely barking out as he turned on his heel, "This is an ante-natal clinic. Go away."

I fled home, tearful and angry, vowing never to go back to the surgery and that horrible man. However, I was dragged back that evening by my mother, screaming and fighting, and had my boil lanced. This was a prime example of a situation where a patient needs sympathy and understanding rather than being told off, sometimes by a dragon of a receptionist intent on defending 'her' doctor, for disobeying rules of which the patient is unaware. It is an incident which often pops into my mind and I have tried never to turn away a genuine patient in need of treatment.

Another time I ended up in hospital was when I was larking about in a field with my pals Jimmy Brennand, Peter Senior and Julie Bagnall (who became Medical Officer for Public Health at the Yorkshire Regional Health Authority). It was another example of my vulnerability to teasing. Jimmy was an inveterate tease. There was some building work going on in the field at the end of Belgrave Drive and Jimmy had somehow persuaded me to go into one of the half-finished houses and look up the chimney to see if I could see the sky. While I was there he threw a half brick which, either by luck or judgement, landed in the chimney and fell on my head, This was my first experience of stitches.

My first experience of the Hull Hospital system which has since played such a big part in my life happened when I was 9 or 10, playing cricket at Hymers. I was cut over the left eye by a cricket ball and taken to Hull Infirmary, then in Prospect Street, by a concerned teacher. We travelled by bus, but when we arrived we were told quite forcefully that we were in the wrong hospital. We should have been at the children's hospital in Park Street. We walked all the way back, Park Street being quite close to Hymers College. Rules and regulations again. Another memory to store and bring out later in life when I had to think about the organisation of hospital buildings and the inconvenience of scattered departments.

Apart from these isolated incidents I wasn't often ill as a child, although I can remember occasionally pretending to be so to avoid school or in one instance purely for pleasure. One year I had met a West Riding girl who was spending a holiday in a caravan in Hornsea. The West Riding had a 'Wakes Week' annual holiday which didn't coincide with East Riding school holidays so I was due to go back to school on the Monday but feigned illness and persuaded my mother to let me stay at home. Later on I said I felt better so was allowed to go for a walk and managed to meet up with the temporary love of my life. I'm not sure what I learned from that episode. To spot malingerers perhaps?

In September 1960 I moved away from home for the first time. Shirley Wainwright's parents had previously taken me down to London to look for somewhere to live as my mother and stepfather couldn't afford the trip. I had scoured the University lists of recommended accommodation and after viewing several had settled on 10, Tamar House, Kennington Lane, where Una Jacobs lived, an absolutely splendid Cockney lady. She was the aunt of David Jacobs, disc jockey and doyen of Top of the Pops. Una was widowed and lived alone. She had once been a barrow lady down the Old Kent Road and Lambeth Walk and had a fund of stories to tell, many of them about her famous nephew, which I enjoyed all the more once I had tuned in to her wonderful Cockney accent. She had a subnormal daughter who was in her thirties and unfortunately a permanent resident in a big Surrey mental institution. Una went to visit her every Sunday without fail, always leaving my lunch ready before she went. She was absolutely brilliant. My breakfast was always waiting for me when I got up and every evening she cooked me a lovely meal. She was so kind and thoughtful, just what I needed for my first eighteen months away from home and Shirley's mother's cooking.

I knew I was likely to have some difficulty in passing my 2nd MB, rated as a very difficult exam and needing a lot of work and, as I've said before, I wasn't a naturally bright scholar. I set myself a target. I would work in the University library from 7.30 a.m. until the first lecture at 9.00, which meant leaving Tamar House at 7 o'clock every morning, walking down Kennington Lane and past the end of the famous Lambeth Walk. In an evening I would work at home until 9.00 then walk down to the local pub for two half pints of beer. It must have worked because I passed with flying colours. But I'm getting ahead of myself. Back to my first day as a student at St Thomas's.

I was early for the Introductory Talk, scheduled for 9.00 a.m. I am always early for appointments. I always have been – a source of just as much irritation on some occasions as being late! I was understandably nervous, a northern boy from a far from affluent home, aspiring to be a doctor, training at one of the most prestigious teaching hospitals in the country. St Thomas' Hospital is just across the river from the Houses of Parliament. Many of the wards overlook Big Ben, a source of delight to some patients when they arrive, but its telling of the hours during long sleepless nights can take the edge off its novelty value. A little further along the river from the hospital is Lambeth Palace, home of the Archbishop of Canterbury, and the famous Lambeth Walk forever associated with the Pearly Kings and Queens.

Standing that morning on the embankment, leaning on the wall, looking down at the Thames and across to Westminster, I pondered on my future. About twenty yards away stood another young man of about my own age who I guessed must be a fellow student. I still had a very broad Yorkshire accent in those days, despite my schooling, having spent most of my spare time either with the Wainwrights, who were West Riding, or on local farms around Holderness where a public school accent would not have been appreciated. I sidled nonchalantly along the embankment until I was within a few feet of him and said "Noo then lad - is'ta goin to't same place as ah'm?" There was no response whatsoever so I tried again. "Is tha goin to be a doctor an all? Ah'm from Yorkshire. This is ma fust day proper in London." He turned then and looked at me. "I beg your pardon?" His accent took me aback but I repeated my question. "Is tha goin to be a doctor?" "I'm frightfully sorry," he said. "I didn't realise you were speaking to me. I'm afraid I'm rather deaf in my left ear." I obligingly moved to his other side and we introduced ourselves. Rupert Drummond came from a Portishead, a very posh area of the west country near Bristol. His father was a Brigadier in the Indian Army, his home background as different from mine as it was possible to be, but we became and remained very good friends.

The Introductory Talk was just like a scene from the film 'Doctor in the House'. The characters assembled there were a very mixed bunch. Two who I met that morning and who also remain my friends were Robin Ballard, another public school boy from an affluent home in Woking, and John Ormesby-Gore who was then in his tenth year and as far as I know is still technically a student, never having passed his Finals. Certainly he hadn't when I met up with him in 1992 at an Old Boys' Day. The definitive prototype for the Donald Sinden character. On that first day of the rest of our lives, as we eyed each other up, we were welcomed by the Dean, and the seriousness of our commitment and the reputation of the establishment which had deigned to enroll us was boomed over our earnest heads. We emerged fired with enthusiasm. Enthusiasm for what depended very much on each individual.

As far as I was concerned it was the beginning of perhaps the most disciplined period of my life. I stuck to my self-imposed programme of study, only taking time off in an evening for rugby training and on Saturdays playing rugby in the afternoon and dedicating the evening to getting well and truly under the influence. But work came first and almost all of it was totally new to me. My introduction to Anatomy was typical. We were taken into the laboratory where there was a line of about twenty bodies, each covered with a sheet. The smell of preserved bodies is quite unlike anything else and remains with you always. We were all apprehensive, most of us never having seen a dead person before. We were split up into groups of four, in our case three men and one woman. Her name was Janet Darling, which inevitably became 'Janet – darling' as we got to know her. She was the daughter of a very eminent Physician. Despite our initial fears we soon became used to working with our corpse and were quite happy to eat our lunchtime sandwiches grouped around one of the tables, discussing the body we had just dissected.

Although Anatomy fascinated me it was strongly linked to Physiology, and to Bio-Chemistry which I found – and still find – boring. Physiology wasn't so bad, although there was one occasion when it was nearly the death of me. Along with 'Janet – darling' I had volunteered to be a guinea pig for a Histamine Test meal. We had to swallow a naso-gastric tube (which we had all had to do as part of our training to see what it was like to be a patient with a tube up your nose!) and then be given a sub-cutaneous injection of Histamine. On this occasion the lecturer gave the two of us the injection intravenously, that is directly into a vein, rather than sub-cutaneously, when the needle is inserted just under the skin, resulting in a very much quicker reaction. Janet went first, then me. As he was injecting the drug into my vein Janet collapsed complaining of a severe headache. Within thirty seconds I was struck by the worst pains in my head I have ever experienced and collapsed, almost unconscious. Histamine is a vaso-dilator – that is, it allows the blood vessels to relax and expand - as well as causing the stomach to release gastric acid. The test was supposed to monitor the change in acidity in the stomach via the naso-gastric tube. Needless to say on this occasion the results were not registered. Janet's father was less than impressed and made his opinions known to the medical school. The test was in fact dangerous in any case because of the massive dilatory effect on the blood vessels to the brain, which caused the violent headache. If either of us had had any weakness in a blood vessel there it could well have caused that vessel to burst, which would have been catastrophic and I doubt very much whether I would be writing this now. At least I found out the hard way what a very severe headache feels like and that my cerebral blood vessels were all right. Whether they still are of course is another matter!

My interest in Anatomy was encouraged by the Professor of Anatomy at St Thomas's, Dai Davis. He was an Editor of Gray's Anatomy, the classic text book for all trainee doctors and nurses. He was a typical Welshman and President of the Rugby Club. At the end of eighteen months study when I took my 2nd MB I came top in Anatomy and was awarded the McSweeney Scholarship. Dai approached me with the suggestion that I should do an eighteen-month BSc Anatomy Degree Course at London University. This was the normal three-year course compacted into a year and a half. He was quite frank about it. I couldn't expect a First, he said, but it would mean that I would be available for the St Thomas's rugby team for an extra year! He said he would help me all he could.

At the end of eighteen months of very hard work I finished up with a 2:1 and a place in the 1st XV! Dai was as good as his word about helping me with the work, conducting tutorials at 8.00am. I was usually all bright eyed and bushy tailed at that hour, still sticking to my disciplined regime, but he was appalling. He was a heavy smoker. I smoked myself at that stage and his first words every morning were "Now then John – give us a fag will you?". If I didn't have any he'd be really upset, hardly able to continue the tutorial.

I had enjoyed playing rugby ever since I had started in the senior school at Hymers and was delighted to be able to continue by joining the St Thomas's Rugby Club. I made it into the 1st XV during my second year, partly due to the encouragement of Dai Davis who seemed as eager to see me progress as a winger as he was for me to get my degree. Of course a very important aspect of the Rugby Club was the social life, an essential release from the hard grind of study. We enjoyed mini-tours during the Easter break, meeting up with other touring sides at various venues around the country. One particularly memorable one was to Cornwall where we stayed in Mevagissey and very quickly became well known to Harold, the landlord of The Ship. One evening, after a slightly heavy drinking session, the whole team lined up on the edge of the harbour then leapt into the sea. We were a sorry sight as we trailed back up the hill to our hotel, wet and bedraggled and still rather drunk. It was the last time we were allowed to stay at that particular hotel.

On the last tour I took part in I remember we played a famous match against St Ives in sub-zero temperatures. It was blowing a gale, sweeping horizontal sleet across the pitch which was situated on a plateau on the side of the hill. I was playing on the wing and I only touched the ball once throughout the entire game when I threw it in at a line-out. By the end of the game I was frozen stiff, almost certainly suffering from clinical hypothermia. The spectators on my side of the pitch were huddled together in little dugouts in the hillside. All I could see of them were their yellow fishermen's Sou'westers as they cheered their side on. At the final whistle I had to be carried off and put in the shower. It was horrendous. On another night, down in Penzance, we had been invited to attend a dance after the game. I was challenged by my team-mates to chat up one of the local girls. I did this quite successfully but our opponents decided rugby was one thing, pinching their girls was another and I was summarily dealt with. I could handle it on the pitch but not off and got quite upset! The Tours were always supported by our chum John Ormesby-Gore who I think was the club's Vice-President. He came from an extremely wealthy family, one of them being Ambassador to Washington. Anyway he was always around, encouraging the lads even though he didn't play himself. His capacity for alcohol was equal to any four of the hardest drinkers amongst us put together.

The high point of the rugby season was the Inter-Hospital Cup. The competition was intense and the day of the final was combined with the annual Rag Parade, always an excuse for all kinds of mischief. Like something out of Doctor in the House I remember once the Guy's students stole the St Thomas's canon, the hospital's 'mascot', and cemented it into the Guy's Hospital forecourt. We sent in a raiding party to try to get it back but the cement had set too hard. After St Thomas's won the cup final they took one of the decorated lorries and drove from Twickenham into London, up High Street to Guy's front lawn and entered into a pitched battle with the enemy with flour bags and the like. Unfortunately members of the public were caught in the crossfire. The last Parade I remember was when some of the students got carried away in Richmond High Street and actually pelted the crowd with flour bombs. The Police intervened and from then on the Parades were discontinued.

Yet another memorable rugby occasion was when I played for St Thomas's against London Hospital in the Finals of the Hospitals Cup. I actually scored a try in that game but in doing so sustained a nasty back injury. I was sprinting down the wing and was cross-cover tackled by their full-back at the same time as the wingman caught me from behind in a pincer movement just as I went over the line. I managed to ground the ball but my body was dragged in two directions and I put a disc out in my spine and had to be stretchered off.

During another match I sustained a head injury and was knocked out completely. I can vaguely remember something happening to me but nothing at all about the game. It was our first match after the death of Winston

Churchill and we had lined up on the pitch before the game to observe a minute's silence. The day before I had queued for five hours in Westminster to pay my respects. The queue had snaked right over Westminster Bridge, along the embankment in front of St Thomas's and back over Lambeth Bridge, so many people had wanted to see the great man lying in state. That I could remember, but nothing about the rugby match.

I was knocked out in the second half but came round and insisted I could keep on playing, even though I was clearly concussed. After the match it was discovered that I was missing. I was eventually found wandering along Richmond High Street, looking for a greengrocer's to buy a pound of apples. I was still in my Rugby kit, dripping wet and covered in mud and talking complete nonsense. I was taken back to the ground, cleaned up then carted off to hospital where I spent four days with severe concussion. I apparently made several phone calls home when I talked total gibberish, a typical symptom of the condition.

The final highlight of my rugby career was being picked for the United Hospitals side to play in the Middlesex Sevens at Twickenham. Playing in front of those packed stands was an unforgettable experience. We actually got to the semi-finals only to be beaten by Harlequins, but it was a great thrill. I retired from rugby when I qualified because I wasn't able to keep up the training, lost some of my fitness and in any case could never be sure of being available to play at weekends. Much later in my career I became involved with 'the other code'. More of that anon.

My friend Rupert Drummond played hockey and the usual Saturday programme after our respective matches was to celebrate our victories or drown our sorrows until we didn't really care either way then pile into somebody's car and drive into London for a curry before going home to bed. On one particular Saturday Rupert and I had been playing at the same sports ground in Cobham in Surrey. During the evening's festivities Rupert was persuaded to do a dance on the bar. Unfortunately he fell off. He complained that his ankle hurt which we all thought was a great hoot. He kept on complaining and we kept on calling him a wimp but we took him home and put him to bed in the house he shared with three other students. I went on home to my digs at Una Jacob's, who was always very tolerant of my Saturday night condition. On Sunday morning I went round to see how Rupert was. When I pulled back the sheets even I was able to make a positive diagnosis of a broken ankle! He had a Pott's fracture, the ankle being very obviously displaced. I called a taxi and took him to Casualty at St Thomas' where he was immediately admitted to have his ankle straightened and pinned under general anaesthetic.

I left my lodgings at Una Jacob's about three months before taking my BSc and moved into a flat in Pimlico which I shared with a chap called Gareth Evans, a very good rugby player but a poor medical student. He played rugby to Welsh National standard and was an exceptional drinker, somewhat of a distraction at a stage when I was working extremely hard. I survived until the end of term then left for my three months vacation which I was to spend as part-time Theatre Assistant at the Westwood Hospital in Beverley. It was there that I met my first wife, whose parents lived in the town and with whom I started a torrid affair. She was my first real introduction to 'women'.

When I moved back to London to resume my studies I joined forces with four other lads in a flat in Prince of Wales Drive. It was 1963, the Beatles were in full song and I enjoyed going to parties on Friday and Saturday nights. Some of the pressure was off as far as studying was concerned and I could relax my strict regime. I began to find the work much more enjoyable, I was enjoying my rugby, I had occasional flings with nurses I met on the wards, Barbara seemed to be enjoying herself back home in Yorkshire and we saw each other in the holidays. Life was good.

I was appointed 'housekeeper' in the flat as I was the only one who could make Yorkshire pudding, an art I learned from Auntie Phoebe. It was a tradition amongst us that everyone stayed in for a Sunday meal, followed by an afternoon or evening entertaining current girlfriends. My flat-mates were the brothers Paul and Robin Ballard, Jonathan Pritchard (who was subsequently to act as my best man) and Richard Olver, a very serious young man. The year was 1963 and I have a vivid memory of one evening in particular when we heard on the radio of the assassination of President Kennedy. It is a very clear recollection – all of us sitting around the table eating my famous Yorkshire pudding when it was announced.

Being able to actually work in a hospital while you are studying is a real learning experience. During our Clinical years we were attached to 'firms' and had the chance to go on ward rounds with the Consultants. We could to a certain extent plan our own programmes with our tutors who guided us throughout the two and a half years. We still had lectures as well of course and the series I found most fascinating was the Forensic Pathology one. These were always scheduled for 8.30 a.m. and were given either by Sir Keith Simpson, author of 'Forty Years of Murder', or by his assistant, Hewlings Johnson. This is when I developed a real interest in Forensic Pathology, in its lurid stories and precise diagnostic procedures. I never missed going to post-mortems during the first half-hour of my lunchtime between 1.00 and 1.30.

The rest of the break was spent eating sandwiches and playing Bridge, at which I became quite skilful. One member of our regular foursome was David Owen, probably the only Socialist in the Students Union at that time and who subsequently became Foreign Secretary in the Labour Government.

Not long before our Finals and before we all left the flat to go our separate ways we had a farewell dinner. We had quite a sociable evening which finished up with a wheelchair race down the main corridor of the hospital, which is about a quarter of a mile long at least. It runs almost the whole length of the hospital which itself extends from Westminster Bridge to Lambeth Bridge. It was to be a race between the students and the Housemen, the porters obligingly turning a blind eye. The young gentlemen had, after all, been working very hard! I don't remember who won.

I do, however, recall rather hazily my stag night. Shortly after taking my Pathology Finals, but before taking my Clinical Finals, I decided to get married. I organised my stag night in the Students Club the night before I was to travel home, arranging for a firkin of beer to be put on the window-ledge and inviting several of my friends to help me drink it. We had already been out to the Eagle on Battersea Park Road to meet all the friends we'd got to know there since it had been our 'local'. We arrived at the club for our evening's drinking, followed by the entertainment which was the Thomas's Derby. It should have been called the Grand National really I suppose. The lounge of the club had about five pillars down each side, with a six foot gap between them and the walls in which were arranged settees, back to back and at right angles to the walls. The tradition on such occasions as this was to race around the room, leaping over the settees. If you fell at a fence you had to drink a pint of beer before you could continue. As you can imagine the races never lasted very long as most participants were incapable of jumping the settees even when sober.

The steward of the club had kindly arranged for me to spend the night there. He put me to bed, knowing which train I had to catch the following morning. I have no recollection at all of being put on the train with my cases at Kings Cross and was only woken at Doncaster by a rather terse lady who asked if I was supposed to be changing trains there. I thanked her and staggered off. "Thank YOU," she said with feeling, presumably glad to get rid of me. I still didn't look very healthy when I arrived at Paragon Station in Hull to be met by my future wife!

DOCTOR GOSNOLD

Newly qualified and now a family man, with responsibilities to be faced and career decisions to be made.

I was married in Beverley on New Year's Day 1966. After a one-night honeymoon in the George Hotel in Grantham we moved into a flat at Curzon Mansions just further along Prince of Wales Drive from my former bachelor establishment. My wife was a fully qualified Staff Nurse and started work immediately at Battersea General Hospital about 100 yards down the road from our flat.

When I qualified I was offered the highly prestigious post as Surgical House Officer to the Dean of St Thomas', Robert (Bob) Nevin, and Mr Lockhart Mummery, at that time General Surgeon to the Queen. That first six months of general surgery was one of the busiest jobs I could have taken on. Junior doctors in recent years have protested, quite rightly, about the sixty or seventy hour weeks they are expected to work but in my first job one week in four we were on duty from Tuesday to Tuesday, a full seven days, twenty-four hours a day, snatching sleep and food as and when we could. Other weeks it was alternate nights on call. The department motto was the same as my mother's, 'work hard and play hard' – not the best recipe for a happy marriage. Not that the faults were all on one side. My wife had always been a very sociable girl and if I wasn't available there were plenty of others willing to fill the gap. I was so busy with work and still so involved with the social life in St Thomas' that I chose to ignore the situation.

Despite the long hours it wasn't a bad life. When possible we had lunch in the Junior Doctors' Mess, waited on by uniformed waiters. I had to be ready to meet Bob Nevin every morning at 8 a.m., waiting to open the door for him as his car drew up outside the private wing of the hospital and able to discuss the patients on his wards. The first 'round' was in the private wing and I needed to have checked on all his patients before he arrived so that they were all ready for him. His 'round of the week' was the Grand Round on Monday afternoon when he visited all his patients with a posse of students, teaching as he went. It was my responsibility to supervise the work of these students, which led to some interesting experiences. The way the Grand Round worked was that a student would be allocated to a particular patient and would have to present that patient's case to Mr Nevin and the other students. Then a discussion would take place about the correct treatment. My job was to make sure that cases were correctly allocated and then afterwards to do a kind of 'sweeping up' operation to make sure all the patients were all right and not confused or distressed in any way.

One such case which sticks in my mind was that of a wonderful lady from Lambeth. She was in her early 60s and had a lump in the parotid gland in front of her right ear. She was a lovely lady – I had already taken a liking to her when I had first seen her in outpatients. She had been on the ward over the weekend in preparation for an operation which was to be performed on the following Tuesday and she had readily agreed to be a guinea pig for Monday's Grand Round. The student allocated to her had taken all her details and started off his presentation confidently enough to the gathering around her bed.

'This is a 64 year old Lambethian woman with a lump on her face. She has a past history of venereal disease. She has had thirteen children and has suffered from two bouts of gonorrhoea and one of syphilis. She spent a short period of time working as a prostitute in Lambeth, smokes twenty cigarettes and drinks half a bottle of gin a day.' You could have heard a pin drop as the Dean, thirty students and all the other patients on the ward listened to this devastating social history. I was aghast. *'And so to her medical history. She has a lump on the side of her face which she first noticed six months ago ......'*

I went back to her as soon as I could to apologise for the details of her personal life having being laid bare before all and sundry. "That's all right duck," she said in her broad Cockney accent and beamed. "Mind you – I just wish he hadn't mentioned me age!" A truly wonderful lady.

I don't know what it is about the women of Lambeth but I have always found them very kind and hospitable. I have already extolled the virtues of my lovely landlady Una Jacobs, but there were others. To survive financially as a student during my clinical year I spent my lunchtimes working in a vegetarian restaurant in Carnaby Street, washing dishes for £2 an hour. I made friends with one of the waitresses who used to slip me the odd free meal and I got to know her quite well. She was married to an Irishman, had one child and she would sometimes invite me to share a meal with them at their house on the Old Kent Road on a Sunday and accompany them to their local for a drink. It was quite a famous pub called the Eagle where several well-known boxers used to train. Such friendly people – I often wonder where they are now.

Towards the end of my six months house job relations at home had become very strained. Then my wife announced that she was pregnant. Things between us were so bad that I in fact questioned whether I was the father, especially as I suspected that she was having an affair with our best man. He and I had been friends for many years and perhaps surprisingly remained so for many more! She was also very close to a certain Indian doctor at Battersea General and when she insisted on calling our first son Jonathan 'Roy' I was a bit put out to say the least.

Jonathan was born on Christmas Day 1967 in Hitchin, Hertfordshire, because by then I had moved on from the surgical job to a medical one at the Lister Hospital in Hitchin. Before leaving St Thomas' Bob Nevin had sat me down and more or less offered me a post as Registrar in surgery back there once I had finished my contract at the Lister. But having done my six months on the surgical wards and observed the backbiting amongst the Junior Doctors fighting for jobs I had decided that it was not for me. I had made up my mind that my future lay in General Practice. I can remember to this day the look on his face as I said 'Mr Nevin, I am going to be a GP.' He said we wouldn't talk any more about it then but would I meet him at his club that evening?

I dressed in my best suit and went along to the club in Pall Mall where we had a delightful meal and afterwards I was invited to 'take port'. Up until then there had been no mention of my career but as we sat down with our drinks he said 'Now my boy ....' and proceeded to try to persuade me of the advantages of surgery. I stuck to my guns, trying to explain why I saw myself as a General Practitioner, until eventually he said he admired my courage and that at one stage it was what he had really wanted to do. However he added that while he thought I would make a good GP he doubted whether it would be a life-long commitment and that at some stage I would return to hospital medicine in some form. How accurate his assessment was – he proved to be absolutely right.

I enjoyed my time at Hitchin where I worked under a Dr Cowan and gained an immense amount of experience in general medicine. As I was the only white junior doctor on the staff I also learned to make a mean curry and enjoyed a very varied social life. I became involved in the production of the hospital Christmas Show, very much as I had been at St Thomas's where they had been quite famous. In those days the St Thomas's show ran for five nights, the cast supplemented by 'guest artists' from Cambridge University. It was the heyday of the Cambridge Footlights and Peter Cooke and Dudley Moore came to give us a hand one year. I was in charge of the lighting and a fellow student, Don Newling, was stage manager. Our paths crossed again a year or two ago when Don was working in Hull as a Consultant in Urology prior to becoming Professor in Urology in Amsterdam.

Another leading light in the shows was Jack Goadby whose father, Sir Jack Goadby, was a Consultant Physician at St Thomas' and had a house on the Helford River in Cornwall. For three successive years in the early 1960s a group of us was invited down to the cottage when Sir Jack wasn't using it and had a hilarious time. The house was quite old and a bit spooky and it was there that I was introduced to the Ouija Board. One night as we were playing with it everyone else let go and I found myself in communication with my late father. I had no doubt that it was absolutely genuine and we 'talked' together for half an hour about my career. I've never touched a Ouija Board since! But I digress.

In the Christmas show at Hitchin I was no longer backstage. Instead I had a leading role. For some reason my wife, who was heavily pregnant, became quite paranoid about it all. She accused me of using the show as an excuse to 'carry on' with some of the nurses, a totally false allegation. I had a lot of fun, yes, but it was all innocent. In the middle of it all Jonathan was born by Caesarian Section on Christmas Day. While still in pain and under the influence of the narcotic analgesia she was visited by the hospital chaplain. "And what are we going to call this lovely little boy?" he asked brightly. "Jesus Caesar?" she suggested. The chaplain said maybe he had better call back the next day!

From February to August 1968 my job at Hitchin combined Casualty and Orthopaedics and it was then that my interest in Accident and Emergency procedures and Psychiatry began to develop. The multitude of different cases that had to be dealt with was phenomenal and there was a huge amount to be learned. I was working with a traditional old Orthopaedic surgeon called Mr Talbot and a new young modern one called Mr Lancaster. Mr Talbot was quite happy for me to run the Accident Department because he recognised that I had surgical as well as medical experience. There was also a Registrar called Mr Mukajee who I didn't like and it was quite obvious that the feeling was mutual. I didn't take kindly to the way he ordered me about! Mr Mukajee is now a Consultant Orthopaedic Surgeon in Scunthorpe, just the other side of the River Humber from Hull and is a respected colleague. Our former animosity is forgotten – almost – and I have managed to get my own back on one or two occasions.

Several cases stick in my mind from those months in Hitchin. First I was taught how to reduce all kinds of fractures by Sister Morris, who was in charge of the department and from whom I learned a great deal. Then there was the case of a little Indian baby who came in and lay for some time on her mother's knee in the waiting room. She had fallen out of a bedroom window and banged her head. She was booked in and no particular notice had been taken of her as she seemed fine but when I came on duty she had been sick and appeared to be asleep in her mother's arms. In fact she had lost consciousness and a quick examination showed she had a fractured skull and an extra-dural haemorrhage. We had no facilities to deal with that kind of injury at Hitchin so an ambulance was called and we set off in a dash down to the Whittington Hospital in North London where there was a neuro-surgical unit. Unfortunately she died on the way, which taught me another valuable lesson about not trusting to first appearances and the importance of appropriate 'triage'. This is the sorting of patients as they arrive in the department into 'clinical priority' which is now common practice in modern day Accident and Emergency work.

The importance of correct triage was also reinforced by the case of a lorry driver who was brought in with breathing problems, having been found collapsed beside his vehicle which was parked on the side of the A1. It was thought on examination by one of my colleagues that he was suffering from a severe asthma attack but when I was asked by the Sister in charge to offer a second opinion I noticed that his neck seemed to be very swollen. What had happened was that he was adjusting the load on his lorry on the A1 when a bar had snapped back and hit him across the throat, fracturing his larynx. By the time I examined him he had surgical emphysema, which is when air becomes trapped between the skin and the chest wall making it feel like a crackly sponge. The only thing that would save his life was an emergency tracheotomy which was duly performed. There was so much to learn and I vowed to keep up my interest in Accident and Emergency, although still determined to go into General Practice.

My interest in mental health was kindled by a patient who came into the consulting room and when I asked him what was wrong he said 'Well, it's the smell doctor.' I could smell nothing but he insisted that he smelled like a lavatory block. He then said that he sometimes looked like a lavatory block. I asked him when he noticed it most and he said when he looked in the bathroom mirror in the morning. I suggested it might be the smell from the toilet but he said no because it smelled even stronger when he was at work. As we talked it became quite clear that he was extremely disturbed and suffering from an Acute Paranoid Psychosis. It was the first time I had had to institute Mental Health procedures and had to call on the assistance of a Mental Welfare Office, (now called an Approved Social Worker). The patient was admitted to the local psychiatric hospital under a compulsory detention order.

I had already had first hand experience of the effects of psychiatric disorder on a personal basis as my mother had frequently suffered from severe mental breakdowns. Even as a child I had realised that she was a bit different from the mothers of my friends. Her behaviour on occasions was quite strange and, as I've mentioned before, she was obsessional about my education to the detriment of the rest of the family. She was also often absent from home, spending long spells in hospital, but at that time I didn't really connect any of these things with mental illness.

As I grew up I became aware of her violent mood swings and that even though she was in general an unemotional person there were times when she was totally *without* emotion. Her moods were reflected in her paintings, some dark, flat and dull, others detailed and sparkling with life and colour. However it wasn't until I went away to university and could view my childhood from an emotional as well as a physical distance that I realised quite how bizarre it had been. By the time she came to live with us when I returned to Hull some fifteen years later I had a much better understanding of her condition.

Thinking about this now I am surprised by a sudden memory of Grandad Hartley, my stepfather's father. I must have been 3 or 4 years old when I first got to know him but even at that age I realised that he was an extraordinarily loud and dominating man who was prone to frequent outbursts of anger. By contrast Grandma Hartley was quiet and timid. Some years later Grandad Hartley was taken ill and became totally confused. I remember seeing him sitting at the kitchen table in his house in Rolston talking complete gibberish and the Mental Welfare Officer coming to see him. He was taken away and I never saw him again, but of course at that time I had no idea what was wrong with him and as is the way with childhood I had forgotten all about it until the memory was triggered by thinking about my mother's illness for this book. Presumably he was suffering from Alzheimer's disease, a condition only now being recognised for the problems it causes in an ever ageing population.

BABIES

Not just mine but back on home territory in Beverley working with the 'legendary' obstetrician Alan Bibby.

On the 1st of August 1968 I moved back home – well almost – to start a nine month term as Senior House Officer in Obstetrics and Gynaecology at Beverley Westwood Hospital in East Yorkshire. It was an exceedingly interesting job, not least because of my boss, obstetrician Alan Bibby. He was a splendid fellow, quite a character and taught me a tremendous amount about surgery, gynaecology and obstetrics. He allowed me a great deal of responsibility and it was stimulating to work with colleagues like Val Player, Ian Jolly and Paul Pearson and an anaesthetist called Julian Bird.

As well as being very busy at work my private life had become pretty hectic as well. Jonathan was nearly eight months old when we arrived and Barbara was newly pregnant and taking it badly. Jonathan was a poor sleeper and quite often would be awake on my return home from work in the early hours of the morning. It was up to me to deal with him while my wife got some rest. As winter came on I could sometimes be seen wheeling him out in his pram at five o'clock in the morning trudging across the Westwood in the snow in an attempt to get him to sleep. The Westwood is an extensive area of partly wooded common land, grazed by herds of free ranging cattle belonging to the Pasture Masters, the roads criss-crossing it protected at the boundaries by cattle-grids, or in one case until a few years ago by a collie dog tethered in a kennel by a long chain. It is a delightful place for a family stroll on a sunny afternoon, but a bit bleak before dawn on a winter's morning.

I got to know the Lodge Porter at the Westwood Hospital extremely well. With all this going on at home it was really surprising that not only did I manage to concentrate on my job but to be quite successful at it. As the only junior obstetric doctor in the maternity unit I had to attend to all the various obstetric crises that arrived from other parts of the hospital's catchment area, which was quite extensive. One crisis that I remember vividly was a lady with an inverted uterus, a condition when the uterus turns inside-out as the afterbirth is delivered. Not only did the Westwood Hospital receive emergency cases from a number of maternity homes without theatre facilities, but the staff of the maternity unit spent part of their time at other hospitals in the East Riding. One morning when Alan Bibby was at Driffield, Val Player and Ian Jolly at Beeford and it was snowing heavily the young woman was brought in from the Woodgates Maternity Home. I knew what to do from reading text books but had never seen, never mind carried out, the actual procedure before. What I did know well was that the most important thing was not to use a Halothane anaesthetic which could aggravate the haemorrhaging which is the greatest danger of the condition. Paul Pearson, our regular anaesthetist, was away. His relief, Julian Bird, was off sick but agreed under pressure to come down to the hospital. Unfortunately he did use Halothane and I was extremely frightened when the patient started to bleed profusely. As a relatively new houseman I was rather diffident about arguing with a formerly eminent consultant but eventually forcefully persuaded him switch to nitrous oxide. The patient had to be transfused urgently while I fought to put her uterus back into position, fortunately successfully, and she made a complete recovery.

Obstetrics is a difficult specialty. It has always been fraught with ethical problems and is now even more so with medical and legal considerations. In those days financial compensation was not such an issue, but difficult decisions were. It is always a hideous dilemma when a baby is born alive but so deformed that there is no chance of survival. Do you allow the mother to see her baby while it is still alive? Or is it kinder to say that it was still-born? What are the pros and cons of trying to keep a very severely handicapped baby alive when it is obvious that it cannot survive more than a few hours or days? I can remember at least two occasions when with the agreement of the nursing staff we did not actively resuscitate such a baby and feel strongly that this was a kinder approach for the mother. Now there are so many pressure groups, often with members who have no practical experience of caring for a severely handicapped child, that a doctor's career can be ruined by the wrong decision, even when that decision is taken in the best interests of everyone concerned.

Termination of pregnancy is another controversial issue, but back in 1968 Alan Bibby had experimented with, produced and perfected a technique using suction apparatus rather than the traditional curettage, which is the physical removal of the foetus with instruments. It is probable that he was in fact a world leader in the performance of suction termination – now a routine operation – but he was completely unrecognised as such. Unfortunately it was fatally easy to be over enthusiastic and puncture the vault of the uterus with the suction apparatus and although taught by the 'inventor' himself, at first I found it difficult to use correctly and on one morning managed to perforate three uteri. One was unfortunate, two clumsy, but three?! One technique I did become very skilled at was forceps delivery using a variety of instruments according to the situation. I was a dab hand with the Wrigley forceps, used in a 'low liftout' situation. Joe Wrigley was an obstetrician when I was a student at St Thomas's and was also the President of the Rugby Club so I had known him well.

It was always a busy job but on my last night on duty at the Westwood my case-load included delivering two breech presentations (where the baby is born bottom instead of head first), one Ventouse extraction (where a suction apparatus is attached to the scalp of the baby and it is literally vacuumed out), one set of twins and then finally at 5.00 a.m., triplets. The mother of the triplets, Mrs Newton, spent two months on the ante-natal ward as we knew she was carrying three babies, but they were not due until after the end of my contract. These days there is very little problem in caring for tiny premature babies, with Special Care Baby Units (SCBU) concentrating on their welfare, but back in the 1960s the policy was to try to delay delivery until the babies reached at least five pounds in weight. Mrs Newton went into labour early and as Mr Bibby hadn't officiated at a multiple birth for several years and also was not at all well he preferred to leave the procedure to me. Happily the three baby boys were all healthy and the mother was fine. By one of those strange coincidences with which my life is peppered, I met the family in Sainsbury's some years later when Mrs Newton recognised me and introduced herself and the family.

In April 1969, eight months into my contract, our second son, Paul, was born in the maternity unit at the Westwood Hospital. He was extremely ill after a very difficult Caesarian birth and remained in an incubator in the special care baby unit for several weeks. During the delivery I was sent for a walk on the Westwood to calm my nerves, but it all happened very suddenly and I arrived back to find myself the father of a very sick son.

As a Senior House Officer I and my family had a flat in the hospital grounds. For my wife it really was 'coming home' as it was where she had trained and she knew many of the staff. The job was extremely busy with only half a day off during the week – Wednesday lunchtime through to Thursday morning. All other nights I was 'on call'. Alternate weekends were free but my off-duty time didn't start until after Saturday morning ward rounds and I had to be back on duty on Sunday evening. In those days the midwives were all-powerful. They expected you to do exactly as they said. Any stepping out of line elicited a sharp rebuke – often justified as they were very skilled at their job and were kept tremendously busy. For me there was a lot of routine work – stitching perineal tears after difficult births and closing abdomens after Caesarian sections – but I learned a great deal about obstetric techniques and difficult procedures.

Working for Alan Bibby was an absolute revelation and surgically it was my coming-of-age. He played a most important part in my life and career. He was a bit eccentric but bright, inventive and not afraid to experiment. Towards the end of my contract I had to cope with most of the work on my own as he was a sick man and had also developed a drink problem which meant that he was either loathe to, or maybe incapable of, turning out at night. Fortunately my observation of his techniques had by then enabled me to cope with most things so that when I failed to wake him by telephone one night to do an emergency Caesarian there was no option but to get on and do it myself. He expressed considerable surprise on a ward round the next day when he saw the lady with her baby and I was able to explain why he had woken up with the telephone clutched in his hand!

He was an exceptional man with great technical skills in general surgery as well as obstetrics and gynaecology. His enthusiasm for his job was tremendous and he ran his own 'Flying Squad' - his Triumph TR4, a fairly new model in 1969. We were responsible for the maternity units at Driffield and at Woodgates Maternity Home in North Ferriby as well as the one in Beverley and every now and then there would be an emergency call from one of the doctors who looked after these units for Mr Bibby to attend someone who had collapsed or who had a retained placenta or an ante-partum haemorrhage. He would dive into his car, throwing his bag into the back, rush to the pathology laboratory which was by the Westwood Hospital gatehouse, grab a couple of pints of O-negative blood from the refrigerator and drive off at breakneck speed to either Driffield or Ferriby. Thankfully I never had to accompany him on one of these call-outs as apparently it was quite an exciting ride!

I mentioned that on one occasion I had to perform a 'Ventouse extraction'. This involves attaching a kind of suction cup to the baby's scalp and pulling on it to assist a difficult birth - a simple but fairly strenuous technique, which invariably leaves a bruise on the baby's head. One night when Alan had been called out to an emergency he had obeyed the summons so promptly he hadn't even stopped to get properly dressed, arriving breathless in his dressing-gown. The extraction was particularly difficult and he braced his foot against the trolley as he pulled, causing his dressing-gown to fall open. It then became obvious that he wasn't wearing anything at all underneath! The expression of the midwife who was assisting him didn't alter at all as she calmly walked round the trolley, reached around him and re-tied his dressing gown. The matter wasn't referred to by either of them either then or in the future.

As I said, Alan Bibby was an inventive man and was a bit of a coppersmith and it was in the shed at the bottom of his garden that he fashioned the series of tubes of different diameters which, if suction was applied at one end would effect a safe method of terminating a pregnancy. He had walked into the hospital one day with this collection of tubes and after sterilising them had attached one end to a suction pump and applied the other to an anaesthetised patient, with excellent result, and from then on we used this method for all abortions at Beverley Cottage Hospital, almost a decade before it became normal procedure elsewhere. Although Mr Bibby was so good at inventing things he never got round to developing or writing up his ideas or presenting them at symposia, so invariably someone else eventually received the credit.

One of my saddest jobs was to deliver stillborn babies, but on the whole it was a happy and satisfying period of my career.

HEDON

My first taste of life as a General Practitioner, ministering to the needs of a rural community in all its variety.

In June 1969 the ambition I had outlined to Mr Nevin in 1967 during my student days at St Thomas's finally became reality – I went into General Practice. The Practice in question was a growing one, based in Hedon, some five miles to the east of Hull on the plain of Holderness. Hedon is a large village with a fine church, an outstanding collection of Civic Plate and a proud history. It was once a port but the ever-changing coastline of East Yorkshire has left it stranded several miles inland. The catchment area for the Practice was mainly rural and stretched across Sunk Island to the banks of the Humber Estuary, which meant that for any patient living more than a mile from a chemist we were allowed to dispense medicines directly from the Practice.

There were three partners in the Practice at that time. Dr Clarke was about to retire, which was the reason for my appointment as an assistant. Dr Graves was a wonderfully bumbling bachelor in his mid-fifties who lived in the nearby village of Keyingham, was looked after by a housekeeper and whose hobbies were his garden and his car. Finally there was Harry Dunn. My contract was for eighteen months in the first instance with a view to a full partnership at its end when Dr Clarke was due to retire. It was quite an old-fashioned Practice. Dr Clarke tended to only see his 'regulars', prescribing age-old remedies he had learned about in his far-off student days. Dr Dunn was overfond of the bottle but Dr Graves was a lovely man, although not renowned for hard work. In addition Dr Marshall, who had been a partner but who had retired, helped out with a surgery on Wednesday evenings. All-in-all, not a very efficient setup.

Soon after I arrived Dr Clarke took me aside and advised me not to be upset if I didn't have many patients when it was my turn to take surgery as most of them were used to the existing partners and unlikely to trust a new young doctor. Within two weeks my evening surgeries were lasting two and a half hours while the others were only seeing a handful of patients each, which was a cause of a great deal of animosity towards me from my colleagues. I found out that quite a few of my patients were exploiting the situation by going to see one of the 'old' doctors for a diagnosis then coming to me to see what I would prescribe. They would then decide which – if any – advice to take. I was caught up in a dilemma. Should I go on prescribing the old-fashioned remedies they trusted or push the modern approach? I decided on the latter, which wasn't particularly popular with the partners, as we shall see later.

Dr Clarke was the senior partner, a widower, not an unkindly man but looking to his pension as he came up to retirement. The Practice at that time provided the official Coroner's Pathology Service in cases of sudden or suspicious deaths in Holderness and it was Doctor Clarke who usually carried out postmortems in either Hornsea or Withernsea. In his absence it was up to me to deputise for him. I had never performed a postmortem before in my life although I had watched a good many. Suddenly it was my responsibility to provide a cause of death and the reasons for my decision, although I was only called upon three or four times during my time there. The most distressing post mortem I had to perform was on a young man who had drowned in Hornsea Mere, particularly poignant for me as it was where I grew up and in view of my own personal phobia about water. His body hadn't been recovered for 24 hours after his immersion and had been prepared for post mortem by Mr Stephenson, whose wife used to entertain my stepfather to breakfast in Hornsea all those years ago! There was no difficulty in giving the cause of death as asphyxia by drowning as about 150 onlookers had seen the young man go under the water and not come up again, having become entangled in the weeds.

As I mentioned, the Practice extended south as far as the Humber and took in such hamlets as Stone Creek and Sunk Island. It was still common practice to deliver babies at home and many of the farming families relied on home-made remedies to cure their various ills. It had to be something really serious to call in the doctor – a reluctance owing much to the days before the NHS when few families had medical insurance and found it hard to afford the doctor's fees or prescribed medication. Before I joined the Practice there had been an older partner called Dr Soutter whose custom had been to make the rounds of the inhabitants of Sunk Island once a week in a pony and trap. Few households had a telephone and communications were difficult so he quite often found patients who were really ill or, on occasions who had died, so his pony and trap had also to act as a hearse. Incidentally there is a street in Hedon called 'Souttergate' where Dr Soutter's father had been in Practice.

This rather laid-back attitude to illness and death took me by surprise after my years in London. We lived in Keyingham, a couple of miles from Hedon and one morning I was contacted at home and asked to go and see a ten month old baby with measles at Cherry Cobb Sands, another of the hamlets near the

Humber. A young baby with measles is quite a serious matter and I arranged to visit immediately after morning surgery. When I arrived at the house and parked my car at about 11.30 the baby's mother was standing outside wearing a blue and white gingham apron, her arms crossed across her ample chest in a defensive attitude. 'Whoo are thoo then?' she asked aggressively and was amazed when I told her I was the doctor. "Bluddy 'ell," she said. "I weren't expectin thoo till next week!" When I examined the baby it was really quite poorly so I put it straight into my car and drove to the Victoria Children's Hospital in Park Street in Hull – the scene of my earlier childhood brush with bureaucracy.

Some calls served a dual purpose. One such was a request to visit a farmer's wife with a sore throat. Surprisingly she wasn't really ill and having prescribed a simple linctus I made to leave. However, her husband suggested we visit his pigs. They all looked very healthy to me and were duly admired but then he confessed that the piglets had 'scour', a common animal diarrhoea, and that he had hoped I would prescribe penicillin for his wife with which he could treat the piglets and save himself a vet's bill!

Megan Davis lived at Rose Cottage, on a corner in the centre of the village of Lelley, about 100 yards down the road from where I now live. I had only been at Hedon about three or four months when there was a call to go and see her as she had bronchitis. Dr Clarke said that if she was asking for a visit she must be at death's door as she never normally bothered the doctor and he asked me to go as soon as possible. I made it my first visit after morning surgery but when I knocked on the front door there was no reply. I knocked again – still no answer and when I tried the door it was locked. If she was too ill to let me in what was I to do? There was a telephone box across the road – should I call the police? I decided to have a look round the back first. As a matter of interest, that telephone box is still there and is one of the very few telephone boxes still to have directories remaining in place!

I knocked loudly on the back door but there was still no response and I was just about to go back round to the telephone box when I heard a loud grunting noise from the barn across the yard. I listened. There it was again. I walked across and peered into the dim interior to be confronted by the sight of a large Charolais cow tied up against the far wall while a lady in a green gabardine coat and black wellingtons was pulling on a rope emerging from the cow's backside. It wasn't obvious at that stage who it was that was doing the grunting. I then realised that she was trying to assist in a difficult calving and that the rope must be attached to the calf's feet. This was outside my experience, although I supposed it was similar in technique to a forceps delivery.

I coughed politely to attract the lady's attention and without slackening her hold she looked round and said "Who are thoo?"

"I'm the Doctor," I said, smiling rather nervously. "I was looking for Megan Davis."

"Aye well, that's me so don't just stand there gawpin', mak thisen useful and come and pull on this bloody rope." I dutifully put down my bag and grabbed the end of the rope and between us with a good deal of effort we delivered the very first Charolais calf to be born in Holderness. That was in 1969.

So what about Megan's bronchitis? It was 'a lot better now' she said and *she hadn't time to be bloody ill.* She was an incredible woman and as my colleague had said, rarely bothered the doctor. In fact it was the only time I met her until I went to live in Lelley more than twenty years later. I was sitting in the Stag pub having lunch one day about two months after we moved in. One of the village ladies of my acquaintance was there with an elderly lady I didn't recognise. She brought her over to introduce me and it turned out to be the very same Megan Davis. She had moved to Kirkella, a village on the western outskirts of Hull, about ten years previously but still came back occasionally to visit old friends. What a coincidence.

The lady who re-introduced us was an example of how people remember you for "just doing your job". About two weeks after Kathleen and I moved in to our new home in Lelley I had walked down to the post box and noticed a lady standing at her front door with her arms folded. As I drew level she said "Noo then - I've bin waiting for you. I knew thoo'd come to live here and I was just aboot to come and knock on tha door. Thoo don't remember me an' me dad do tha?" I had to confess that I did not.

"Well," she said, "Thoo's the best doctor that ever was. Thoo looked after me dad when he was dying".

Then I remembered. She had nursed him diligently through his last illness and I had visited them on a regular basis. He had had terminal cancer but they had both wanted him to stay at home. All I could offer was pain relief and support but she had never forgotten it and now she was saying 'thank you' again twenty-five years later.

On the day that we actually moved to the house in Lelley, with furniture vans in the drive and total chaos inside the house, a bloke came across the road and said "Hello John. Nice to see you again."

It was one of those situations when you know you should know who someone is but can't for the life of you put a name to the face. I played for time and said, over-brightly I'm sure, "Hello - nice to see you too. How are you?"

"Fine," he replied. "Look - I can see you're busy right now. Perhaps we can have a pint later on?"

I nodded eagerly, still desperately trying to remember where I had met him before. Once in and partially unpacked we introduced ourselves to our neighbours and I said, I hope casually, "By the way, who lives in the first house up there on the right?"

"Oh that's Paul Owen," she said.

Then it all came back to me. Here I was moving in opposite to the lad I'd shared Methodist holidays with all those years ago, the lad I'd spent ten years at school with. We hadn't seen each other since we left Hymers College at eighteen. Yet another coincidence. But I'm getting ahead of myself. Back to my GP days in Hedon.

A call to a farm at Boreas Hill one night at 11.30 was interesting and had repercussions for the next twenty years, until the retirement of cardio-thoracic specialist Mr Moghissi in fact. The call had come from the distraught wife of a farmer who had arrived home from the pub and had collapsed in the farmyard complaining of chest pains. I rushed out to the farm immediately and found that he had been vomiting profusely. At first I thought that he was just very drunk and that the chest pains were due to the vomiting, but having helped him into the house it was obvious that it was something far more serious. Laying my hand on his chest I could feel surgical emphysema, that is air underneath the skin around the upper part of the chest and the lower part of the neck. The only way this can happen is if the lower part of the oesophagus is torn by violent vomiting, known as the Mallory-Weiss syndrome, a very rare and dangerous medical condition which I had seen only once in my student days, but which the symptoms seemed to fit. I called for an ambulance straight away.

Knowing that it would take it at least half an hour to reach the isolated farmhouse I rang Mr Moghissi at Castle Hill, the hospital on the western outskirts of Hull specialising in heart and chest cases. It took a while to find him but eventually he came on the phone and I explained who I was and that I was sending him a 67 year old emergency patient with a Mallory-Weiss tear in his oesophagus. A rather haughty voice told me that such things didn't occur just like that and that I was clearly overstepping the mark as a new boy and would I please send him to Casualty at Hull Royal Infirmary. I was so sure of my diagnosis that I lied and said that the patient was already on his way even though the ambulance hadn't actually arrived by then. When it did I despatched the patient to Castle Hill and went home to bed, gloomily anticipating a reprimand the next day. However, the phone rang at 3.00 a.m. and a rather different sounding Mr Moghissi congratulated me on my diagnosis and said if he hadn't been able to deal with the patient so promptly he would have died. As it was he was doubly lucky as the condition can be fatal even with immediate action. The congratulations were very gratifying, but Mr Moghissi had a more tangible momento of the night as every Christmas for many years after he received a turkey from the grateful farmer, ironic in view of the fact that he had originally not wanted to treat him. I got nothing but the phone call.

As I settled into the Practice I began to understand more about my partners and their habits and had my first serious disagreement with Dr Clarke. It was over the prescribing of drugs and medicines. I tended to prescribe modern commercial remedies, simple things ready packaged in bottles or packets with the instructions clearly printed on the labels. The profit in the mainly rural Practice came from the pharmacy with extemporaneous mixing of basic ingredients, the pharmacist's wages being paid by the Family Practitioners' Committee. Dr Clarke insisted that the Practice policy should be adhered to, but I refused to comply, insisting, rather pompously perhaps, that my prescribing habits were based on the needs of the patients rather than the profitability of the Practice. He countered by pointing out that my salary depended on that profitability so it was in my own interests. Despite that, I persisted in my prescribing and ironically the pharmacist agreed with me. He surmised that many of the mixtures he dispensed were usually used for feeding tomatoes, changing the colour of hydrangea flowers or treating animals!

Dr Clarke was right though, my salary such as it was did depend on the Practice making money and I set about thinking of ways of achieving this. The income of a GP comes from two sources; the 'capitation fee', (that is an annual basic payment for each patient registered with him) and 'item for service' payments for such things as immunisations, vaccinations, cervical smears and medical examinations for industrial tribunals and insurance. Dr Clarke agreed that the latter had potential and we soon had a thriving 'well-patient' clinic going long before they became popular, and the Practice income began to rise. Strangely though there seemed to be no corresponding increase in profitability.

Gradually I came to realise that as I rushed around the rural patients one partner's car would invariably be parked outside a village pub around lunchtime, usually the Stag's Head at Lelley, now *my* local. The excuse was always that he was visiting one of the publican's family but this wore a bit thin after a while as the car would often be parked there for a couple of hours or more. A detailed look at the distribution of visits between the partners and a more careful check on the car soon revealed that Dr Dunn's visiting list consisted almost exclusively of public houses. The knowledge that Dr Dunn was also responsible for the accounts for the Practice increased my anxiety. Further investigation was obviously necessary, especially as my bank manager was making unfriendly noises about my increasing overdraft. The purchase of our first house and a car had stretched my resources beyond the limit and I urgently needed to increase my meagre income. I pointed out to the bank manager that as he also looked after the Practice accounts he must know that my income was secure and that I had every anticipation of becoming a partner. His reply was disturbing, implying that the future economic prospects of the Practice were not good and I would do well to restrict my spending and, in his words, live on baked beans.

I ascertained that the books were kept in a locked filing cabinet in Dr Dunn's consulting room, but when I did manage to get a glimpse inside it one afternoon all that could be seen was a bottle of gin. It was at that stage that the wisdom of becoming a full partner began to be cast in doubt, confirmed when I read the contract. Dr Clarke had decided to stay on part-time and still draw 25% of the profits of the business, so I would be working round the clock to finance his retirement, whilst at the same time supporting Dr Dunn's drinking habits. Dr Graves just liked his roses and petunias - and perhaps his housekeeper! So instead of signing a contract to become a partner I found myself looking round for another post.

At that time Hedon was renowned for a rather scruffy wooden-shacked estate called Bond's Estate where some rather odd families lived and where none of my colleagues was keen to take his car because of the deep potholes and ruts along the unadopted road. I gradually became aware that I was being called regularly to one particular house to treat an 18 year old girl for a variety of minor illnesses. She was not highly intelligent but was quite attractive. Soon she began to write to me, at first complimentary letters thanking me for treating her, then increasingly hostile when on occasions I had refused to visit and finally downright rude with abusive personal comments. The crunch came when she visited the surgery and flaunted her charms in front of me. I asked her to leave, refusing to examine her without the presence of a chaperone and adding that there was no indication that there was anything wrong with her. This prompted a final damagingly hostile letter, but fortunately I had filed all her previous ones and discussed the case with my colleagues. On this occasion they fully supported me and agreed that she should be removed from our list but it was a lesson to be learned about the vulnerability of young doctors and made me establish a rule to which I still adhere. I always have a second person with me when examining or treating a woman patient on her own, whether at home, in the surgery or in hospital and it is still part of my modern day teaching.

With a rural practice it is a principle which is sometimes difficult to apply. Once a week we held surgery in the front room of the vicarage in Burstwick, a nearby village. Chaperoning then had to be carried out either by the patient's relative or by the vicar's wife. There were no such things as Practice Nurses. Two evenings a week surgery was held in another front room in a house in Bilton on the outskirts of Hull. This was very busy and there was no vicar's wife to help out so it was even more difficult. Somehow I survived all the traumas and grew fond of many of my far-flung farming families, but a decision had to be made. It was time to move on.

YORK

My first and last experience of running my own practice, complicated by a deteriorating private life.

Despite all the problems in Hedon I was still convinced that my preferred brand of medicine was General Practice and I started seriously seeking a post where I could be my own boss. I saw an advertisement for a single-handed general practice in York, went over to see it and was immediately taken by its situation in a beautiful Georgian house with a lovely garden in Bishopthorpe Road. Dr Reid, the incumbent, needed someone to take over urgently as he had had a heart attack and then suffered a cardiac arrest in hospital. Although he had recovered he was not able to continue working. I gave my colleagues in Hedon two weeks notice and without further ado moved into the house in York which went with the Practice.

The retiring GP already had a cottage in Hutton Sessay into which he and his wife moved immediately, leaving behind his housekeeper and the lady who helped to run the Practice. The latter however was quite happy to retire so that my wife, a qualified nurse, could take over. The Practice, although single-handed, shared a weekend and night rota with two neighbouring Practices, a very convenient arrangement which gave each of us two nights off every week as well as two weekends out of three free.

Initially I really enjoyed the job in York. I was a free agent, able to run the Practice as I wished and build it up over the four years I was there. It was quite small – about 2,300 patients – and very much part of York's 'South Bank' community. It covered Bishopthorpe Road, South Bank and the Terry's Chocolate Factory area, running right up to the Knavesmire, plus a few wealthy patients in Bishopthorpe itself, where the Archbishop of York has his Palace. One of these was the only private patient registered with the Practice. His name was Harry Brown – that much I knew – but I didn't see anything of him for the first two years I was there. Then his wife called me one day to say he was suffering from severe abdominal pain and had been very sick. The vomit, she said, was dark brown, so it was almost certainly blood.

When I arrived at his house he was clearly quite ill, bleeding from oesophageal varices, almost certainly the result of prolonged heavy drinking and leading to Portal Hypertension, secondary to Hepatic cirrhosis. I organised his immediate admission to York County Hospital and when he said he wanted to go into a private hospital and could pay the bill I told him I didn't take private patients. I also told him that I considered that to be admitted to a private hospital would be dangerous in his condition because of the absence of a resident physician.We had a bit of a confrontation, both of us sticking to our guns and finally I said if he didn't want to be treated by the NHS he could transfer to another Practice. He decided to accept my decision and stay with me. He did in fact, stay with me for many years and became a very good NHS patient.

Another interesting call was to Bishopthorpe Palace itself where one of the gardeners who was a patient of mine had suffered an accident. The Archbishop's wife called me. The victim had been taken to the palace drawing room into which I was ushered with great formality to see this lowly member of the household staff. His injury in fact was fairly minor and I was able to reassure his employer that he would be able to resume his duties quite quickly!

During our time in Keyingham my wife had been kept fully occupied looking after our children, although she was never altogether happy or satisfied with being 'just a mother' or at being stuck in a small rural village. In York she quickly became more part of the community and more actively involved with the Practice. Looking back it is clear that this was the point at which our marital problems began to escalate. She wanted to play an increasingly active part in the Practice and I was determined that she shouldn't become too clinically involved. I was happy for her to help with the administration and organisation, but she wasn't satisfied with that. Social conditions in our area of York at the time were pretty poor and so I decided that with her help we would try and get improved play facilities for the local children. We successfully negotiated with the Council to allow us to set up an Adventure Playground on the waste ground behind the house and I managed to persuade several local builders' merchants and garage owners to donate wood, old tyres and building materials. Soon a very active recreation area was up and running, largely under her supervision. The Council, once they saw how successful it was, decided to set up a voluntary agency to manage the playground on a more formal basis and employed a man called Kevin Curley to oversee it. The second time Kevin entered my life was in Hull several years later when, after my wife and I had separated, he moved in with her and the children. Over the years and without my knowledge she must have continued the relationship which had started in York.

One of the early difficulties we had with the playground was that of access. The only entrance to the land was from the end of the street which ran along behind our house, which concerned some of our neighbours as lorries had to use the street to bring in the materials needed in the construction. Even when that was finished some of the youngsters using the play area were less than well behaved. However, the local vicar was keen on the scheme and became involved in it, lending it an air of respectability.

The Practice, as I have said, was not very large and the area it covered was quite compact so that I could easily walk on my daily rounds. Just like Hedon, there was a legacy of traditions in the area, but in this case I had to work them out for myself as there was no-one to tell me about them. Once established I tried to quietly introduce one or two more modern concepts. Soon after I arrived I appointed a Practice Nurse who was invaluable not only in helping to run the surgeries but also in undertaking some of the home visits. We were soon able to increase the 'items of service' payments and the extra income generated more than covered her salary. My wife was annoyed at being left out and suggested setting up a leg ulcer clinic. This was a good idea as there were many elderly patients on the books with the inevitable problems of poor circulation, varicose veins and obesity, a sure recipe for leg ulcers. After the initial diagnosis there was little I could do for them that couldn't be taken care of by a competent nurse and it satisfied her desire to be involved.

It was through this clinic that she met 'Auntie Joan'. Joan was a very large lady, more than eighteen stones in weight, who was employed at Terry's Chocolate Factory and had devastatingly bad ulcers. She had been attending the surgery for years without any noticeable improvement in her condition. My wife regarded this as a challenge and a chance to prove her worth. Joan lived with her two sisters. None of them had ever been married and were very old-fashioned and set in their ways. Joan suffered from depression and clearly did not look after herself properly. My wife was sorry for her and incredibly suggested that she should move in with us as she said Joan didn't get on with her sisters who bullied her. Her justification was that we could do with more help in the house. I wasn't impressed by the suggestion, but, willing to do almost anything for a quiet life, I reluctantly agreed and Joan became a fixture in the household. She was very possessive and appallingly unhygienic, but my wife was obsessed with curing her so that was that.

I have to admit that she was useful as a baby-sitter, freeing one of us to go out in an evening and both of us to go out together on my nights off, but she gradually became a real problem. She had terrible black moods, was very manipulative and more difficult to handle than a child. My wife however was thoroughly enjoying being more involved in the social scene.

We had been in York about two and a half years when 'Malcolm' entered our lives. He was a seventeen and a half year old psychopath who had spent

85

much of his life in detention centres, but in between he was one of my patients. For some reason my wife decided that here was another challenge, that she could take him in hand and reform him, and he too moved into the house, occupying a small spare room. It wasn't that we didn't have plenty of space – it was a large Georgian house – but he was another real problem and led me a merry dance. I tried to convince him that as he was now part of the family he should behave appropriately, but he wanted all the privileges without any of the responsibilities and he and Joan soon fell out. Joan resented him and the two of them fought for my wife's attention like spoilt children. Chaos reigned and eventually I could stand it no longer and said he would have to go. He packed his few belongings and left but in the middle of the night he broke back in, shinning up a drainpipe and climbing in through Joan's bedroom window, frightening her half to death and causing a great furore.

One of my reasons for evicting him had been a suspicion that his relationship with my wife was more than a professional or even social one, confirmed when I had found her in his bed. She said that she was frightened of him and that he had threatened her with a knife but I was not convinced. His next ploy was an attempt at suicide by slashing his wrists. He was taken to the casualty department of the County Hospital but proceeded to run outside and climb a drainpipe up onto the hospital roof. I was called to try to persuade him down and at that point my private life became rather public. My wife's behaviour was beginning to affect not just my personal life but my credibility within the Practice. My Practice Nurse, Eunice Mowett, who was aware of the true state of affairs, was very supportive and a good friend, but even she could see that it was an impossible situation and prepared for the inevitable by accepting a post as a nurse at York University.

In a way all of these events which caused me to consider a move were in fact a blessing in disguise. Despite all my innovations I was secretly becoming bored with the daily routine of general practice and had been seeking outlets for my wider skills, one of which was undertaking two sessions a week in the Casualty Department of the County Hospital. I found myself looking forward to these sessions more and more and thoroughly enjoying the variety of problems with which I was faced. One such was a coach crash in nearby Helmsley in which a day-trip for a group of elderly folk ended in disaster when their coach ran out of control down a steep hill. Many people were brought in with serious multiple injuries, a real challenge not only of resuscitation but of organisation.

On another occasion I was called to the British Rail carriage works in York where an employee had trapped his hand in a large seat-making machine in which spiked round drums fed the backing material onto the leatherette for railway carriage seats. The man's hand had become trapped and his arm had gone round behind the drum, between it and the metal protecting plate, pressing him upright against the machine. An ambulance had arrived but it was impossible to extricate him from the drum and they had called me as being the nearest doctor. I gave him a pain-killing injection, then we set about releasing him.

With some difficulty we got the metal guard plate off, only to find a six inch block of solid oak running along behind it, holding him fast. I could see that his arm and hand were very badly mangled and bleeding heavily. The whole scene began to take on the air of a rather bad horror movie. His blood pressure was dropping and he was beginning to lose consciousness. I realised that the only thing to do was to amputate part of his arm as far down as I could reach. I had no surgical instruments with me so asked if anyone had a sharp knife. Someone produced a twelve inch one, obviously used in some manufacturing process, and as my intentions became clear the fifty or so interested spectators magically disappeared, leaving just three or four stalwarts prepared to help me. As rapidly as possible I cut off the man's mutilated hand so that we could free him from the machine and lie him down, at which point he began to regain consciousness.

I went with him in the ambulance to the hospital, relieved that at least we had been able to save his life, only to be confronted by the orthopaedic surgeon who asked why I hadn't brought in the severed hand so that it could be sewn back on! Instead of arguing I drove back to the factory, waited while they finished extricating the mangled remains of the hand, then took it back to the surgeon and asked him if he performed miracles as well.

It was these events which influenced the kind of jobs I began applying for when it became obvious that I could no longer stay in the York Practice and paved the way for my eventually abandoning General Practice for the much less predictable 'Accident and Emergency'. The name had been changed from 'Casualty' in 1963 when Sir Harry Platt identified in his 'Report Into Casualty Services in the United Kingdom' that people were attending for medical conditions as well as accidents. The life and death decisions, the sorting out of priorities, treating a different set of people every day, all satisfied my desire for variety, for new challenges, for testing my skills to the limit. Once again it was time to move on.

Before the Flixborough explosion.

After the explosion.

The sad effect that a chemical explosion and the toxic after effects can have on a human body.

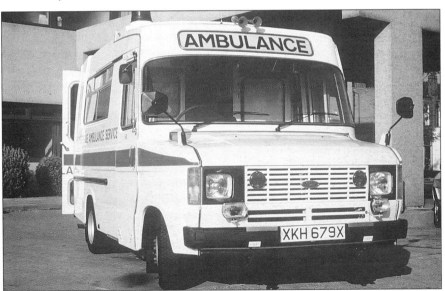

The magnificent service that try to help the victims. This is the Flying Squad vehicle "31" from the Humberside Ambulance Service.

The entanglement following the Flixborough Disaster. These pictures show the extent to which a chemical factory can be damaged by an explosion followed by a fire.

CASUALTY

Back to the hospital scenario and the beginning of the rest of my life in Accident and Emergency as I return to the City and County of Kingston-upon-Hull.

As soon as I saw the advertisement in the British Medical Journal for a Registrar in the Accident and Emergency Department of the Victoria Hospital in Blackpool I drove over there to talk to Mr Wright, the local Orthopaedic Surgeon in charge. I had no recent experience of working within a hospital apart from my sessions in York Casualty. It was 1974, just four years since I had left Hedon, four years in which I had been my own boss. Could I readjust to working as part of a team? I talked to Mr Wright at length and the upshot was that he offered me a one-year contract at the princely salary of £3,260 per annum. There was no special training package at that time for accident and emergency personnel. I would have to rely on my general medical skills and deal with the unfamiliar as and when it arose. I was giving up a lovely Georgian house in a historic city, an established Practice which I had considerably enhanced during my four years stay, and a salary of between £12,000 and £14,000 a year for a poorly paid job with no security in a noisy seaside resort. No wonder the family were not amused.

The most noticeable feature of Blackpool was the almost total absence of patients during the winter months – the odd broken wrist when an elderly resident had a fall – and the frenetic activity in the summer as the influx of merrymaking holidaymakers and day trippers flooded into the department at the rate of over 300 a day. Many of the complaints were minor such as cuts from broken bottles, fight injuries, sunburn or sudden ailments, but because they were away from home the victims didn't have access to a normal surgery so they landed up on our doorstep. More serious injuries were occasionally caused by the trams which ran along the promenade, an unfamiliar phenomenon to many of the visitors even when sober and certainly not treated with respect when they had had a few drinks. On at least three occasions I had to take a Flying Squad from the hospital to the seafront to extricate people from underneath trams. I remember these experiences because it was like walking into a theatre, the lights blazing and a huge audience attracted by the spectacle of a disaster on a hot summer's day. The trams were in fact potentially lethal, running almost silently through the noisy crowds with no barriers of any kind to protect them.

Another memory is of Glasgow week, a general holiday in the Scottish city when many Glaswegians come down to Blackpool for their annual holiday, bringing with them their own policemen to try and keep any over-exuberance in check. One night after the pubs had closed there were an appreciable number of Scottish visitors in A&E, accompanied as usual by a member of their constabulary. One Scotsman, very much the worse for drink, became abusive to a nurse. The policeman came up behind him and unceremoniously hit him sharply over the head with his truncheon, whereupon he dropped unconscious to the floor. We subsequently had to keep him in overnight to treat that injury rather than his original one! It was also during my year at Blackpool that my interest in child protection issues crystallised. Following the 1973 Maria Colwell inquiry, knowing that I already had an interest, the hospital authorities asked me to lay down procedures for child protection in the hospital, a subject I will return to in a later chapter.

The Specialty of Accident and Emergency was at a key stage of development and many new procedures were being initiated. I have already mentioned that there were no official training courses, partly because accidents and emergencies cover such a wide field, and I determined to develop my own training package. As part of this project I spent several sessions down at the local venereology clinic which, as you can imagine in a place like Blackpool, was very busy. The consultant in charge was a bit of a character. One day a lady came in who, when asked how she thought she had contracted the disease, said she thought she must have got it from her bicycle seat. He responded by asking her whether she had brought the bicycle in with her for diagnosis!

Towards the end of my year's contract, once again, I had to start looking for another job. One advertisement that I saw was for a Consultant in A&E at Redhill Hospital in Surrey, on the outskirts of London. I drove down there and talked to another orthopaedic surgeon, a Mr Ring, famous for the development of the Ring Hip Prosthesis, a replacement hip joint. The job itself sounded quite interesting but it was clear that what Mr Ring really wanted was for someone to run the fracture clinic and take care of some of the simpler orthopaedic cases rather than to run the A & E Department. Also one glance in an Estate Agent's window made me realise that we couldn't afford to move down there, but I went to the interview anyway and was questioned by a panel which included a gentleman by the name of Howard Baderman, Consultant in A&E at University College Hospital. I wasn't offered the job, somewhat to my relief, but afterwards Dr Baderman sought me out and said he thought I was rather overqualified for it and suggested I look for something nearer home. Since then he has advised me several times during my career, always with sensible down-to-earth suggestions.

The next job I applied for was in Warrington in Lancashire. The interview was at the headquarters of the North-West Regional Health Authority in Liverpool. I was sitting waiting in an ante-room when in walked John Allen, a doctor I knew well, who was at that time a Consultant in the A&E department of Hull Royal Infirmary. He had held the post for nearly a year and like me was looking for a change. As we sat chatting rather nervously one of the interviewing panel walked by and winked at John. I looked at him curiously. Was this perhaps a set-up job? Who can tell. Whatever, he was the successful candidate at the end of the day, which logically meant that there was going to be a vacancy in Hull.

That evening I rang Dick Berkin, a consultant orthopaedic surgeon in Hull, whom I had known when I worked in the maternity unit at Beverley Westwood Hospital. I used to refer babies born with a congenital dislocation of the hip to him and he had always responded well to my interest in the cases. I re-introduced myself, told him I was working in Blackpool and asked him whether he was aware that there would shortly be a vacancy in A&E at Hull Royal Infirmary. He said no. Not surprising really as John Allen could hardly have handed in his notice already. However, I had registered my interest and when the post was advertised some months later I applied and was short-listed. The interview was in Harrogate, and I was offered the job.

During the interview I vividly remember the Assessor from the Royal College of Surgeons looking at me over his glasses, acknowledging my long experience in General Practice but querying my brief time in A&E. Had I, for example, ever had to do an emergency tracheotomy? My response was that I had; one, and I then questioned whether *he* had, or indeed ever known it to be necessary? I suggested that there were very few occasions when it would be necessary as there were various alternative ways of managing an impeded airway. I had to eat my words in 1995 when a Russian seaman was brought into Hull Royal A&E after being crushed by a heavy container on the docks. He had obvious airway problems and after the anaesthetist had paralysed him he then attempted to get an endotracheal tube through his larynx, but without success. It became apparent that his larynx was ruptured and that the only solution was a tracheotomy, just like the occasion I had been involved in all those years ago in Hitchin. And so at 6.00 a.m. on a Sunday morning in 1995, after nearly thirty years in the profession, I performed my second and hopefully my last emergency tracheotomy. My patient survived and eventually returned to Russia having had his larynx reconstructed. A tracheotomy, in which you have to quite literally cut the patient's throat, is very much a last resort and life saving procedure. But as usual I digress. Back to 1975.

We moved back to Hull in September of that year and after a brief stay in a rented house in Astral Gardens in Sutton we bought 1009 Anlaby Road on the city's western outskirts. It was here that my encounter with my grandparent's former neighbour, Mrs Phillips, took place. I was very lucky to have been appointed to a Consultancy without any higher qualifications, although whilst I was in Blackpool I had become an MRCGP (a Member of the Royal College of General Practitioners), a qualification based on my years of experience as a GP and at that time acceptable as a qualification for entry into A & E. I was in fact appointed before there was any formal training programme available for Accident and Emergency, but the Government had agreed to appoint thirty A&E consultants throughout the country in a somewhat belated response to the report prepared by Sir Harry Platt in 1963.

Essentially what had happened was that at the inception of the Health Service, Casualty Departments provided a completely open-ended service to anyone who wanted to drop in. More casual than Casualty. Way back in 1958 the British Orthopaedic Association had published a report expressing anxiety regarding the staffing of Casualty Departments. Sir Harry was then commissioned by the Government in 1963 to look into the matter and prepared his report which basically said that the word 'Casualty' should be done away with and the departments should be called 'Accident and Emergency', acknowledging the considerable number of acute medical conditions that were treated, such as the victims of heart attacks, strokes, diabetic comas and epileptic fits. Under the new system the Casualty Departments at hospitals such as Beverley Westwood, Hornsea, Withernsea, Bridlington and Goole were re-designated as 'Minor Injury Units' while Hull Royal Infirmary became a 'Major Accident Department'.

Sadly Sir Harry also recommended that at that stage all these units should continue to be overseen by an Orthopaedic Surgeon. These surgeons were really 'caretaker managers' and did not take any personal interest in the departments under their care, so in 1968 the government agreed to appoint thirty consultants specifically to Accident and Emergency, or 'A & E' as it quickly became known. I think I was number thirty! These consultants were drawn from all branches of the profession – surgery, medical, anaesthetics, orthopaedics – with three or four of us from General Practice. Soon after this a training programme was established and the Casualty Surgeons'

Association, established in the mid 1960s, changed its name to the British Association for Accident and Emergency Medicine. There is also now a Faculty with its own Specialist Registrar Training Programme and an exit examination into the Specialty of A & E, the CCST, (Certificate of Completion of Specialist Training).

So began the most important phase of my life. I was to remain a Consultant-in-Charge in the A & E Department of Hull Royal Infirmary for the remainder of my medical career. It has embraced a wide variety of major accidents and emergencies as well as the daily routine, when we treat on average over 250 patients a day or 85,000 a year. As A & E Consultant I have been responsible for co-ordinating the control of all major disasters in North Humberside, now East Yorkshire, and in the case of another war – which God forbid – would have been responsible along with the Public Health Department for all emergencies. When I started in the Department I was single-handed, assisted by thirty sessional part-time General Practitioners or Clinical Assistants. Now there are four full-time Consultants, one part-time Consultant, five Specialist Registrars, five Staff-grade Doctors and twelve Senior House Officers as well as sixty-five nurses, eight porters, thirteen receptionists and two secretaries. Inevitably it is not enough, especially when major disasters such as the explosion at Flixborough, the dreadful fire at Wensley Lodge in Hessle or the Lockington train crash occur.

The Flixborough explosion in a chemical factory in South Humberside, now North Lincolnshire, happened before I returned to Hull but as a 'local lad' and a doctor I read and heard about it. I remember being appalled by the morbid sightseers whose parked cars hampered the emergency services in their efforts to reach the scene. Sightseers always flock to disasters – I referred to them gathering around the victims of the tramway accidents in Blackpool. The fire at Wensley Lodge took place when I had been back in Hull for just over a year. The big old house in Hessle was home to fifty elderly men and when fire broke out at about 9.30 on the evening of Saturday January 5th 1977 eleven of them died, trapped on the top floor. Nineteen were badly injured and brought into Hull Royal.

At the time the alarm was raised I was in a pub in Tickton (a village on the River Hull near Beverley) so I was called on my bleeper and was told that there was a major disaster involving the Wensley Lodge Retirement Home. On my way in to Hull Royal I was given more information by car radio from the Ambulance Service, so en route I was able to assemble the personnel I needed at the hospital to deal with the situation in the shortest possible time.

text continued on page 105

Otley Hall. The family home of the Gosnold's for many years.

The memorial plaque in St. Mary's Church, Otley which commemorates the memory of John Gosnold, Gentleman Usher to Queen Elizabeth and King James (circa 1600).

The village sign of Otley, Suffolk, supported by the current John Gosnold.

The sign to Martha's Vineyard near the ferry terminal on the mainland of Massachusetts.

'Memories' of the Vineyard Indians from 1660. A burial ground on Martha's Vineyard.

A tribute to Bartholomew Gosnold; the ship named after him in 1632.

Kathleen, my present wife, wearing the most attractive smile.

God grant me the serenity
to accept things I cannot change,
courage to change things I can,
and wisdom to know the
difference.

A stone in the Aboriginal Cemetery at Alice Springs, Australia. This almost certainly epitomises my present philosophy on life above any other, indicating a significant change in beliefs over the last decade.

The grave in Mappleton church yard where Clarice Edna was buried in 1940.

The headstone of that grave, presumably replacing the old one in 1994, after Jim had been further married to: Florence Edna and Auntie Ethel and then lived with Mrs Stephenson. "Lucky Jim" - "Reunited" What goes around comes around!!

The scene further up the track at Lockington showing the complete devastation even a small train can sustain if it hits a car.

The car hit by the Bridlington to Hull train on the morning of Saturday 26th July 1986.

The carriage on its side overlying a ditch at the track side, showing the only way in.

The inside of the carriage showing how disorientating it can be to work in a carriage on its side

As an operation it went very well but it was extremely distressing to see the bodies of the elderly men being brought in and knowing we could do nothing for them. The living came in large numbers and we set about resuscitating them where necessary, treating them for shock and finding them beds. I learned several things that night about the availability of facilities for the elderly. When I had enquired earlier that afternoon there had been no beds available to receive patients but that evening we managed to find space for some thirty-odd survivors. Where had all the previous occupants gone we wondered? Had there been thirty unexpected deaths, a flurry of discharges, or had the department been less than frank about bed availability? Something perhaps to be investigated!

The smell of scorched human flesh is quite unique and once experienced can never be forgotten. Soon after taking up the post in Hull I developed a close relationship with John Settle, Consultant in charge of the Regional Burns Unit. He commented to me one day that he was seeing a lot more of me than of my colleagues in other districts and that the incidence of house fires in Hull appeared to be very high. It culminated in my being called into the Casualty Department one morning in the early hours to treat the victims of a suspected arson attack on a house in Selby Street, virtually across the road from the hospital. The victims were the three Hastie brothers and the smell of burnt human flesh has remained with me to this day. It pervaded the whole department for hours and hours.

The boys were fully conscious and in very little pain because the burns were 'full thickness', thus acting as their own anaesthetic as there were no nerve endings left to send messages to the brain. However, they were so extensive that there was no way the boys could survive. I still have a vivid memory of my feelings of helplessness and hopelessness as I talked to them, knowing that the outlook was so terribly grim. It was quite heartbreaking and that memory and the attendant smell are imprinted permanently on my mind.

The throwaway comment made by John Settle about the high numbers of victims from housefires in Hull led to a discussion with the Humberside Police and a fresh look at some of the incidents.

Arson was unearthed! It is vital for the medical profession to cooperate closely with our police colleagues.

EMERGENCY

The birth of the Flying Doctor Service, the tragedy of the Lockington train disaster and the lessons to be learned.

In 1969, while I was in General Practice in Hedon, I had been called to a very nasty road traffic accident on a straight stretch of road between Keyingham, where I lived, and the hamlet of Ryehill. One person was killed and two others were trapped in their cars. There was very little I could do without suitable equipment and it forcibly brought home to me how important it is to have resources at your disposal at the earliest opportunity. Quite literally it can be the difference between life and death. I had already heard about Ken Easton, a GP in Northallerton in North Yorkshire, who the year before had set up an 'immediate care' scheme to deal with the regular accidents which occurred on the nearby A19 trunk road. There was a move to follow his example in Hull and the East Riding, motivated by Dr Mackenzie who lived on the A63 in Gilberdyke and who also saw frequent accidents almost on his doorstep but could do little to help until the ambulance arrived.

Julian Bird, anaesthetist at Beverley Westwood Hospital, who I have mentioned before and a doctor called Paul Pearson, another Beverley anaesthetist, were both interested in pre-hospital care. They and the Chief Ambulance Officer for the area got together a few doctors to set up a local 'immediate care' scheme. A meeting was held in 1969 at Longcroft School in Beverley, attended by representatives of the medical profession, ambulance, fire and police services. By the end of the meeting the Yorkshire and East Riding Voluntary Accident and Emergency Service was born, later, by popular consent, to become known as the Flying Doctor Service. When I officially 'retired' after thirty years of involvement I was presented with a memorial plaque.

The main advantage of our scheme when it was set up was that the ambulance service was totally involved and that each doctor was provided with an ambulance radio. My own car rapidly turned into a kind of First Aid ambulance service of its own, complete with green and red flashing lights and a boot full of equipment. From then on any accident which occurred in East Yorkshire could call on the nearest 'Flying Doctor' to attend, saving valuable time. As I was one of the few doctors in the scheme who lived to the east of the city the call came quite often, ably supported by John Wilkie another GP who lived in Keyingham. His wife, Jean, who is still alive and present when

I was presented with the memorial plaque was a huge stalwart of the team of ladies who raised money to support the scheme, as was Nora Bird, wife of the anaesthetist Julian Bird.

Although I left for York soon afterwards, more seeds of interest in Accident and Emergency procedures had been sown in my sub-conscious. They lay more or less dormant during my years as a GP but then sprouted and grew in Blackpool, finally flowering when I returned to Hull as a fully-fledged consultant in 1975. During the intervening years things had progressed and soon after I took over the department at Hull Royal Mr Fozard, the new Chief Ambulance Officer, agreed to let us have an ambulance dedicated exclusively as a Hospital Flying Squad vehicle. It was converted, equipped and maintained by voluntary subscription as the NHS would not fund such a vehicle.

All Hull ambulances have a numerical call-sign. Ours was to be '3-1'. Shortly after it went into operation a cartoon was circulated around the ambulance service and the hospitals. It depicted an ambulance with various inscriptions on its side, one of which was 'The Gosmobile'. It was backed up with its doors open to a cemetery gate through which a team of ambulance men was carrying a coffin. Someone who looked suspiciously like me was standing at the gate of the cemetery carrying a medical bag. The caption read 'He'd try to resuscitate anything'. Far from being offended I was delighted that our service was perceived in such a positive light, with people recognising that, while humour prevailed, we were all doing our best to improve *First-* aid and *pre-*hospital care.

At that time the job of the Miller-trained ambulance crews was to get the victims to hospital as quickly as possible. There were no fully-trained paramedics in the ambulance service and only the Flying Doctors had resuscitation equipment, so '3-1' was the best of both worlds. Today of course, with the improvement in communications and technology, ambulances can respond more quickly and are manned by medically trained personnel. They can deal immediately and efficiently with cardiac arrests and accident trauma. Care in the community has also improved out of all recognition so that the chances of surviving a heart attack or an accident are greatly improved and the need for a service such as 3–1 is considerably reduced.

During the '3-1' years there were many interesting and even amusing incidents as well as the tragic ones. There were the difficult cases where victims had to be released from machinery or cut from crashed cars by firemen while we did our best to treat them in situ, sometimes for an hour or more. These situations were always horrible, dirty, noisy, risky and full of pain, with the added frustration of working in a severely limited space while trying to stabilise patients and alleviate their distress. At least it equipped me both physically and emotionally for situations I came across when not on duty, which I will come back to in a later chapter. The main thing is to be able to adapt medical and sometimes surgical procedures for use in a completely alien environment in order to preserve life until you can get the patient to the hospital.

Of course not all of our call-outs were to traffic accidents. The word 'collapse' covers a multitude of conditions from hysteria and fainting fits to shock and cardiac arrest. One Saturday evening we were called to Reckitt's Social Club in East Hull where the firm's annual dance was in progress and we rushed in enthusiastically, all bright eyed and bushy tailed, carrying all our equipment. The team consisted of me, two nurses and the ambulance crew and we were eager to prove our worth. The band was playing a slow fox-trot and the big silver multi-faceted ball, obligatory in the centre of the ceiling of any self-respecting dance floor in the days before strobe lights, was showering the scene with a confetti of light. The only light. As our eyes adjusted to the near darkness we were led through the dancers to the centre of the floor where a small group of people were surrounding an elderly man who had clearly had a heart attack. Two of them were making a not very successful attempt at cardio-pulmonary resuscitation, probably inspired by half-remembered scenes from the popular television series Emergency Ward 10, starring local lad John Alderton.

Despite the lack of light I managed to get access to a vein while, in the best tradition of the Titanic, the band played on. One vital piece of equipment we carried was a portable defibrillator, a machine which applies an electric current to the chest to stop the uncoordinated twitching of the muscles of the heart which prevents it from pumping blood around the body, resulting in cardiac arrest. Fortunately this piece of equipment was self-illuminating so we were able to tell immediately that the patient was indeed in a state of 'ventricular fibrillation' and to give him several DC shocks. Thankfully his heart regained its regular rhythm and his colour began to return to normal. Deciding at this point that discretion was the better part of valour we loaded him onto the stretcher and beat a hasty retreat from the dance floor with our patient and equipment. The dancing had continued throughout and obviously most of the revellers had no idea of the fact that one of their number had lain dying in their midst.

Another call-out to a place of entertainment was to the Astoria Bingo Hall in Holderness Road in East Hull. Again we rushed in with all our paraphernalia, responding to a reported collapse. We ran into the foyer and were directed by an attendant up into the auditorium of what had been a cinema. It was the first time I had ever been in a large bingo hall. We were ushered round the backs of the seats as play continued, the Caller's amplified voice filling the building, the players crouched over their cards with frightening concentration, pens poised to make the triumphant final mark. To add to the unreality the Caller interrupted the proceedings when he saw us and asked the audience to stand and give us a round of applause as we made our way with difficulty to the lady who had collapsed. Once we reached her however they lost interest and play was resumed. We carried out our resuscitation procedures to a background of clickety-clicks and legs elevens. We managed to stabilise the patient, loaded her onto the stretcher, gathered up our equipment and stood up to leave whereupon the whole standing ovation procedure was repeated. Quite bizarre.

Even worse was when we attended an incident at a much smaller club at the back of premises on Anlaby Road in the city where it was the Caller himself who had collapsed. He had had a cardiac arrest while in full flow, but by the time we arrived a replacement had been found and play had resumed. Two members of the audience were trying to revive the unfortunate victim on the stage, only partly screened by a curtain. I couldn't believe that they expected us to treat the patient in full view of everybody while they continued with their game. Sadly on that occasion we were too late. The gentleman had called his last number.

Completely different was the incident at a farm where a worker had fallen into a grain silo, a huge container for the storage of loose corn. When we arrived the only parts of him still visible were his head, shoulders and arms and from a distance he showed no signs of life. Death in this kind of case is quite horrifying, caused by compression of the chest which prevents breathing so that in effect victims suffocate with their faces uncovered. I was lowered down on a rope to assess the situation. He had no pulse and clearly before we could have attempted resuscitation he would have to be have to be extricated, a dangerous, difficult and lengthy procedure as the grain would have to be drained from the bottom. All I could do was confirm death.

Another incident I was called to was reminiscent of the one in the railway seat-making factory in York. This time it was in a meat factory in Anlaby on Hull's western outskirts where a man had stumbled into an unprotected gully in the factory floor which contained a 'wormer' – a huge and very powerful metal spiral which revolved continuously to carry waste products along the duct. The cover which normally prevented accidental access had been temporarily removed, probably to clear a blockage, and the man's foot had been caught and his leg dragged almost a couple of turns around the screw before the machine had stopped. He was completely trapped and it was a case of giving him an anaesthetic so that the machine could be reversed to release him before we could treat him.

A situation I personally had difficulty with was when I was called out to the BOAC animal feed mill near the city centre where a man was perched on top of the chimney threatening to jump. When I arrived the fire service had already prepared their hydraulic platform into which I stepped with two firemen – and some trepidation – while it was lifted to its full height. Now I do not like heights, even moderate heights, without something solid under my feet. Fully extended this swaying platform on the end of a flimsy looking metal arm was at the right level but still some ten feet out from the top of the chimney. The man looked at us and repeated his intention of jumping. As we talked to him the platform was inched nearer and nearer to the chimney until we were as close in as we could get. At that height moving laterally is not a smooth operation, it is more of a jerk and sway, like some mediaeval dance, and my knuckles were white as I clung to the guard rail, feigning calm and fighting nausea. In short I was terrified.

After some discussion during which the man flatly refused to join us on the platform it was decided that I should join him on top of the chimney. There was only a one foot gap but as far as I was concerned it could have been a hundred. As I stepped onto the chimney the man appeared to step off the other side – not however into space but onto the access ladder, a sort of fire escape with little platforms at intervals between the zig-zagging steps and up which he must have climbed originally. I stepped back onto the hydraulic platform, which resumed its surreal dance until we were round the other side of the chimney and once more in touching distance of our prey. At this point one of the firemen said 'Right Doc – why don't you just knock him out with one of your drugs?' I silently diagnosed 'Too much James Bond' while contenting myself with a rather terse 'Not a good idea'. I didn't feel it was quite the right time for lengthy explanations as to what could happen if I were to render the man unconscious, even if it had been physically possible. Mental visions of his inert body hurtling to the earth, in all probability taking me with him, were not comforting at this stage of the proceedings.

Plan B was for me to stay where I was while the two firemen dealt with the situation, which seemed to me a much better idea all round. One of them climbed onto the ladder and managed to grab hold of the man whose hands were firmly clamped onto the rail, which he refused to release. The other fireman climbed out and swung himself up underneath his colleague, kicking at the man's hands until he had to let go, then the first fireman literally threw the man onto the platform next to me where I was able to hold him until they both climbed back in and the four of us were lowered to the ground. By the time we reached solid earth I think I was in a worse state than the patient. To the firemen it was a routine operation and they couldn't understand my terror. We were 'The Flying Squad' and as such expected to be able to cope with any situation but we were trained in medicine, not in the many other skills needed to be a member of the Fire Service or the Ambulance Service. And I am still terrified of heights.

Of course all these incidents, dramatic though they were at the time, pale into insignificance beside the events of Saturday 26th July 1986. I was on duty in the Accident and Emergency Department when a call came in to say there had been a train crash at Lockington, a pretty village in the Holderness countryside east of Beverley. They requested the assistance of the Flying Squad so we assembled the team and set off. As we drove along further information was relayed to us. It was rather more than just a simple train crash, a not infrequent occurrence in the county in those days when many rural level crossings were unmanned. Apparently there were quite a few people involved in this one but at that stage the ambulance service did not think that it constituted a 'major accident'. Had it been designated as such, to comply with the 'major accident' guidelines I would have had to return to the hospital to organise the Department. We made the decision that the most important thing was to get to the scene as quickly as possible so that we could assess the situation for ourselves. We increased our speed and decided to take the shortest route, through the middle of Beverley, an ancient market town with the traditional weekly Saturday Market held in the square in the town centre. It is very popular and so very busy but because of Lockington's location to the east of Beverley it is still quicker to go through rather than take the by-pass which loops around the town to the west. Unbelievably, in view of the situation, we were later criticised by a Beverley Councillor in a letter to the Hull Daily Mail objecting to the 'noise of emergency vehicles travelling through the centre of a picturesque market town on a busy Saturday morning'!

When we arrived at the end of the lane leading to the scene of the crash there was a Police car blocking the road, manned by a young policewoman who had had the foresight to prevent sightseers driving to the scene and causing the access problems experienced at Flixborough, to which I referred earlier. She was later to be commended for her actions which undoubtedly helped all the emergency services to reach the victims as soon as possible. Indeed a fair number were already there when we arrived at a scene of seemingly total chaos, and many of the minor casualties had already been taken to Bridlington hospital on a bus, organised with commendable speed and efficiency by British Rail.

The first victim I saw was a dog, lying dead at the side of the track near to the level crossing over the narrow road, the site of the actual accident. Bits of a wrecked vehicle were strewn along the track and further on I could see railway carriages heaped up in haphazard fashion like a child's carelessly discarded toy. One carriage was lying on its side over a ditch parallel to the torn and twisted rails, pointing in the wrong direction, and it was here that we were taken, the majority of the serious casualties being in that carriage.

The train was a four-car diesel unit, the 9.33 a.m. from Bridlington to Hull. The schools were on holiday and many of the estimated 300 passengers were families with young children. The train had collided with a Ford escort van at the unmanned level crossing and was the worst of three major accidents on that stretch of line in seventeen years.

The only way into the overturned carriage was through the front window of the driver's cab. It was bizarre and disorientating to stand upright and look down the length of the interior with the roof-racks on one side and the seats on the other, the windows above and below me. It was a case of picking your way along the frames trying to avoid the shattered glass. There was a firemen ahead of me peering along the carriage and several more working to free passengers who had been thrown through the windows into the ditch beneath the carriage as it twisted and turned in the air, somersaulting before it came to rest on its side. There were still some people trapped inside as well and I treated these first as they were released. One was a very elderly gentleman who was understandably totally confused.

I can remember at this stage having a discussion with the ambulance service personnel as to whether we should even now officially declare this a 'major accident' in view of the number of casualties, but I was assured that the normal services available were coping. I learned later that the hospitals could have coped even better had major accident procedures been in place with the consequent extra staff being made available, but of course all that was in hind-sight. At the actual scene all the emergency services had responded with commendable speed and performed brilliantly.

Over the following two or three hours the firemen in particular commanded my total respect. Just as I do not like working suspended in space at great heights, neither did they choose to work with severely injured and even dismembered bodies. Thankfully even for me this is not an everyday occurrence but I can to some extent view them as 'patients', as problems to be solved. I worked closely with the firemen as they cut through window frames and twisted metal sheets to get down into the ditch where the bodies lay. We were still not certain at that stage whether there was anyone left alive and never gave up hope that there might be, but my job was mostly to confirm death. Perhaps the most poignant find in this devastating scene was a pregnant lady with severe abdominal injuries – a new life snuffed out before it had properly begun. I had to crawl down through a broken window to work my way along the ditch. The noise of the cutting machines was deafening, it was dirty and dangerous, very hot and very distressing, but I was extremely proud of the way everyone at the scene worked together.

Later as I walked along the track talking to a senior police officer we reflected on the fact that this was the first time since the Flying Squad had been set up that we had had to deal with anything of this magnitude and that there were lessons to be learned, notably about early decisions on activating the major accident procedures. When the chemical plant at Flixborough on the south bank of the Humber blew up the Humber Bridge wasn't built. As I've said I was at the time still working in Blackpool, but had the bridge been in place I am sure that Hull Royal, as the major accident centre for the region, would have received most of the casualties and procedures may well have been revised then. The medical problems on that occasion were of course of a quite different nature as the volatile mixture created by the water from the firemen's hoses falling on the burning chemicals corroded everything it touched, including human flesh, adding to the problems of severe burns.

On the positive side we learned that when the chips are down people will work way beyond their own line of duty and regardless of their personal safety. We also noted that perhaps the most crucial decision of the day had been taken by PC Carol Dyson, the young policewoman who was first on the scene and had blocked off the road to all except emergency vehicles to protect the access route – vital to the success of such a complicated situation when journalists, camera crews, freelance photographers, onlookers and even well-intentioned volunteers can seriously hamper the work of the professionals as it had at Flixborough. She also kept information flowing to the various command posts of all the organisations involved, enabling the best use to be made of their resources. She was subsequently commended by the Coroner at the inquest who said she had brought credit to the Police Force.

The bald statistics of the accident were that, of the 300 passengers, 9 died and 37 were injured. The train travelled 150 yards along the track after colliding with the van. It was the worst rail accident in Britain for two years and involved 60 firemen, 11 fire appliances, 3 emergency trailers with hydraulic lifting gear, rams and cutting equipment, and 10 ambulances and their crews. The foster-son of the driver of the van was one of the fatalities. The first casualties arrived at the hospital at 11.20 a.m., just an hour after the impact, and the last of the bodies was not released until the evening.

In the aftermath several issues arose which received extensive coverage in the media. The row sparked off by the letter about the emergency services going through Beverley rumbled on, with complaints about shoppers having to flatten themselves against walls as the vehicles rushed through. Would they still complain, I wondered, if the ambulance was trying to save the life of a member of their family? The fire service in turn complained about being held up in the town and queried whether parking regulations should be reviewed.

Several months after the accident I attended a Memorial Service in Lockington Church. I think it was a very important occasion for everyone who had been involved. It was really the first time that we began to think seriously about 'stress counselling', something which these days is taken for granted in almost any distressing situation and indeed thought by some people to be overdone, with even distant relatives of people involved demanding counselling and often financial compensation as well. As if a price can be put on emotional distress! Be that as it may, while for many years help had been available for bereaved relatives and surviving victims of major accidents, the stress caused to the professionals involved had been largely ignored. Maybe the time had come to take a long hard look at the pressures on members of the medical profession of not just the occasional but the ongoing stressful situations they had to deal with and the effect it had on their work. Certainly the experiences of that afternoon left an indelible impression on my mind and led indirectly to the writing of this book.

Where on earth can you land on this? You can't. Let's hope the wire is strong enough!

Easier to land on this. At least H marks the spot!

The cricket match in progress from which I was snatched away on that Sunday afternoon.

The Eagle has landed! Receiving a patient on the landing site at the Hull and East Riding Rugby pitch, sadly no longer available.

Dr Ian Jolley and myself, along with Jean Wilkie, Nora Bird and George Stokoe, all connected with the Yorkshire and East Riding Voluntary Accident and Emergency Service, (lovingly called the "FlyingDoctor Service" by the Hull Daily Mail who were presumably short of ink!) receiving retirement shields in 2001.

HELICOPTERS

The good, the bad and the ugly side of being on call to attend accidents and emergencies on ships and rigs in all weathers.

One of my other duties as A&E Consultant at Hull Royal was to accompany the Search and Rescue helicopters, based at RAF Leconfield a few miles north east of Beverley, whenever one of their missions required a doctor. It was my first contact with the armed forces since my schooldays when I had been in the Combined Cadet Force, the CCF – not by choice, membership was compulsory. Presumably it was supposed to be 'character-forming'. It was that kind of school. I chose what I thought would be an 'easy billet', the artillery section of the Army Cadets, a small squad who looked after the school's 25-pounder gun, but as soon as possible I joined the band and learned to play the bugle. I quickly improved enough to be promoted to head bugler, with a silver bugle instead of the normal copper or brass.

I vividly remember one occasion when I had cause to regret this vaulting ambition. We were at Catterick Camp in North Yorkshire along with cadets from many other schools in the north east. The silver buglers had to take it in turns to sound reveille, which was supposed to be a great honour. We didn't consider it as such however, as we had to be up, dressed in full regalia and standing at the end of the line of tents at some unearthly hour of the morning. Having theoretically woken everyone up we then had to make sure the occupants of our own tent were making a move. The morning of my turn was foul. It had been a stormy night and most people were already awake. It was still teeming with rain and I was disinclined to get dressed and stand outside to get wet through. So I took a shortcut. I stuck my head out of the tent and sounded reveille while I was still in my pyjamas.

Unfortunately that was the morning the Sergeant Major decided to do early morning rounds. I remember the bugle suddenly disappearing from my hand in mid toot and a large red face adorned with a ferocious moustache being thrust through the tent opening. A very loud voice asked in no uncertain terms what I thought I was doing and without waiting for an answer barked 'Captain's tent, 9 sharp'. That little escapade earned me a whole day 'spudbashing' and the loss of my silver bugle for a year.

Despite this the following year I was appointed drum major, in charge of the mace. The school corps was to be inspected by the Major General of the North East – a very high honour indeed. We had practiced for weeks and my tossing skills had been honed to perfection. After visiting the various sections, our illustrious visitor mounted the dais on the parade ground ready to take the salute. As mace-bearer I would be leading the parade in front of not only the MG but the headmaster and assembled staff, local dignitaries and of course our proud parents.

I had been told by Captain Taylor – who in real life was our woodwork master – that I could toss the mace as much as I liked as we marched along the back and up the side of the parade ground, but that as we turned to cross in front of the platform I should just hold it steadily aloft. Now that was a bit of a blow after all my practising. I had been throwing well as we marched around the ground and as we made the second turn I decided that it would be a shame for the audience to be deprived of a close-up of my skills. As we came level with the dais I tossed the mace up really high but the wind caught it right at the top of its spin and it became obvious that it was going to come down behind me. And it did. About a yard behind me, landing point first and sticking into the ground where it swayed gently back and forth as the band swerved around it, followed by the rest of the cadets struggling with their mirth. As we wheeled right for the last time and turned into the quadrangle to dismiss, it still stood there accusingly upright. Fortunately it was right at the end of my final term at the school so the repercussions were minimal, but I learned a valuable lesson. In a military situation when someone in authority says 'jump' you jump. You don't stop to argue and you don't decide that you know a better way of doing it. This was to stand me in good stead in my various missions with the helicopter crew, when not jumping on command can be fatal.

Obviously because of Hull's position near the mouth of the busy Humber estuary on the perimeter of the North Sea, most of our call-outs were to ships or oil and gas rigs, and to start with I found it all very exciting as it presented me with many interesting problems. Whenever I got the call on my bleeper from RAF Leconfield I would have to make my way as quickly as possible to Hull and East Riding's rugby ground at the Circle on Anlaby Road, only a few hundred yards from the hospital. It was a cricket ground as well and until the late 1970s had county status, being the venue for some memorable Yorkshire matches. However it had a limited capacity and the pitch suffered from its winter use so sadly it was demoted, but it made an ideal and convenient temporary heli-pad. When the copter touched down I had to be ready, kitted out in my flying suit and with my medical bag fully packed, so that I could climb aboard with the minimal delay and we could head for whatever location had requested assistance.

One such request was to a trawler about 20 miles off the Danish coast. A crewman had been hit by a swinging hook which had caused a severe head injury and knocked him out completely. By the time we got out there he had regained consciousness but was obviously concussed – a condition where the victim is quite irrational, has no control over his behaviour and can be violent. It is unwise to sedate a patient in this condition as the combination of drugs and a head injury can cause complications. We loaded him on board with some difficulty and he spent the next hour trying to throw us all out of the helicopter! Another interesting trip was to a Faroese fishing boat where a crewman had trapped his arm in the roller system of the winch down in the hold. I had to wade through thigh deep cod and haddock to get to him and give him a local anaesthetic injection so that I could work the winch backwards and release him.

When someone has a heart attack on board a working boat it is unusual for them to survive because of the time it takes for a doctor to reach them. However on one occasion we were successful in bringing a fisherman back alive from a trawler off Bridlington. He was very lucky in several respects. The distance we had to travel was relatively short, the first aid he had received from his mates had been good and his heart had re-started before we arrived so that we were able to stabilise him and fly him back to hospital.

Calls to the mouth of the Humber estuary can be interesting. Sometimes trawlermen find themselves at sea when they sober up after a night on the tiles but decide that they would rather not go on that particular trip, so they have an 'accident', or develop mysterious symptoms requiring immediate medical attention. No skipper can afford to set off on what could be a long trip with a sick crewman on board so they call out the helicopter. One man we attended had allegedly fallen down the companionway into the hold and hurt his back, so we took him off. By the time we landed back in Hull he had made a remarkable recovery It was tempting to fly him straight back to his boat!

Sometimes we are called to foreign ships, which can cause problems other than plain language difficulties. On one occasion I was asked to attend the wife of the Master of an Iranian oil tanker, who had started to have a miscarriage. Because of their religious beliefs Muslim women are not allowed to be treated by a male doctor but she was haemorrhaging badly and her husband had to convince her that there was no alternative. I went in waving my stethoscope in front of me and repeating 'Doctor, Doctor' in an effort to reassure her. I made a very superficial examination while she remained fully clothed to make sure that she was fit enough to travel, set up a drip and loaded her into the helicopter. We flew her straight to hospital where she could be treated by a female doctor.

I had a lot of interesting trips during the years I served with the helicopter crews but there were a two or three which finally made me decide I had had enough. The first was an epic which lasted a great deal longer than the normal couple of hours. The call-out came when I was at home at about half past three one sunny Sunday afternoon. The RAF had been asked to fly the mission as the Bristow's helicopter which would normally have taken it was grounded because of bad weather. I looked out of the window in disbelief. There wasn't a cloud in the sky. The request for assistance had come from an American gas rig to the south of our area, almost opposite the Wash. When I boarded the helicopter the pilot told me that although it was fine inland there was fog out to sea so he was going to climb to 3,000 feet – very high for a helicopter which normally cruises at about 700 feet above ground level. We cleared the coast and almost immediately saw a great bank of fog below us. We made our way down to the area of the incident and the navigator explained to me that one of the blobs on the radar screen was the rig, the rest were ships. We dropped down and as we entered the fog bank we realised just how dense it was and manoeuvred very slowly.

We had been told that the patient we had been called to had a 'severed leg'. I had learned from experience that this could mean anything from a minor cut to the actual loss of a limb, but until I was able to see for myself I had no idea how urgent it was to get the man to hospital. We crept lower and lower and as we neared sea level our progress became even more cautious. There is a rule in helicopter flying that you are not allowed to fly below 400 feet unless you can see the land but over the sea the rule doesn't apply. At that moment I wished that it did. Anyway eventually we could just make out the waves which couldn't have been more that 60 or 70 feet below us. All we could see was water and swirling fog. We started to move very slowly towards the biggest blob on the radar screen, soon picking up a smaller blob close by which the navigator said was the rig support ship. We established radio contact with them and the skipper said they would guide us in to the rig. This involved the pilot hovering close behind the stern as we inched our way forward. After what seemed like hours but can only have been about 20 minutes the ship's skipper said he dare not go any closer and we were on our own.

We still couldn't see the rig and with the wipers going full speed visibility through the windscreen was impaired, so the winchman opened the side door and sat on the edge peering out through the gloom. We were just about to give up when he said he could see one of the legs not more than 50 feet away. The trouble was we didn't know which leg it was. This was important as the landing pad sticks out from the top of one of the legs and we needed to know which way to manoeuvre. By now we had established radio contact with the rig and the Master guided us up the side of the leg and across to the next one where we put down on the heli-pad. Everyone released their held breath and the pilot said he would be quite pleased if I didn't spend more than 20 minutes sorting out the patient as he would really rather like to take off again as soon as possible!

The journey from the heli-pad to the medical room is quite tortuous, up and down steep slippery ladders and steps and along narrow corridors, and it took me three or four minutes to reach the medical room, which meant that I only had about ten minutes to deal with the casualty. Fortunately it was a well equipped rig and the resident medic had efficiently bandaged what was a very deep gash in the crewman's thigh, but he was still in considerable pain and had lost a lot of blood. In the short time available I got some fluids into him intravenously, gave him a painkilling injection and had a quick look at the wound which very fortunately hadn't severed the bone or the major artery. I decided it would be safe to move him but because of the difficulty of access we strapped him upright to a chair. We managed to find a route back up to the helicopter which although slightly longer didn't involve quite so many steep steps and we were back on board in just under 30 minutes.

The next decision was where to take him. It was relatively easy to fly straight up off the rig and climb back to 3,000 feet and sunshine but at some point we were going to have to land again and by now the fog had encroached even further inland and several airports were closed completely. Norwich was still open however and this seemed to be our best bet. We radioed ahead for an ambulance and it was there to meet us when we touched down and whisked our patient off to hospital, leaving us to refuel. Leconfield had said they were still open – maybe. We decided to try for it and took off as quickly as possible, listening as reports came in of first Manchester, then East Midlands and finally Humberside airports all declaring themselves closed. The pilot tried going down below the fog over the sea so that he could approach Leconfield as low as possible but by the time we reached the mouth of the Humber we could see that it was impossible so we turned around and went back to Norwich, which was still open – but only just.

One of the advantages of the Sea King helicopters is their extra fuel capacity and consequent longer range so there were no worries on that score. The crew were quite nonchalant about the whole thing and said there was no problem, we would just check into the airport hotel for the night. *Slight* problem, I said. Once I took off my flying suit, which had integral boots, I would be wearing my gardening trousers, a tee-shirt and what were by now very sweaty socks and underpants. Not the nattiest attire in which to arrive at a 4-star hotel. The pilot's solution was to radio ahead for 'footwear for the Doc – size 8'. And when we arrived at Norwich sure enough there was footwear waiting – a pair of long black size 8 wellies! So at 11.15 p.m. I checked in looking – and probably smelling – like a stablehand. We had been operational since 3.30 p.m. and we were tired, hungry, dirty – and thirsty. First things first. We made for the bar where a reluctant barman was persuaded to make us a huge tray of sandwiches which the five of us polished off in double quick time. During the next hour or so I was privileged to witness the unbelievable capacity helicopter crews have for beer. I made no attempt to keep up with them but did wonder, wearing my professional hat, how long it would be before their blood alcohol levels dropped enough for them to be fit for duty. At least I wouldn't have to breathalyse them!

When we finally retired for the night I discovered that hotels are used to dealing with visitors who appear with only the clothes they stand up in. Plus, in my case, borrowed wellies. There was a complete toilet kit laid out in the bathroom. I cleaned myself up a bit then dropped into bed and slept like a log. Next morning I shaved with the hotel razor, cleaned my teeth with the hotel tooth brush, showered with the hotel shower gel and splashed myself all over with the hotel after-shave, but still had to dress in my disgusting clothes, including the wellies. I went down to breakfast feeling very self-conscious amongst the pin-striped suits, crisp shirts and club ties of the commuting business men. There was no sign of the crew but the waitress had obviously been primed and treated me with great kindness. When my mates finally put in an appearance they didn't look at all out of place in their air-force gear.

The weather was still bad and apart from that the pilot said he had received orders that he was to stay in the south to fulfil a special mission, so secret that he could tell me nothing about it except that he estimated that we wouldn't be back in Hull before 4.00 p.m. I was horrified as I had a day filled with appointments but I had no option but to accompany them as they flew to RAF Coltishall, where we sat around reading the papers and chatting to the other crews. There was a good deal of banter between the Leconfield and Coltishall boys. There is always great competition between them about the number and complexity of missions flown and their success rate. It was rather like being in the midst of a group of teenagers from rival schools. Finally a decision was taken – I'm not sure who by – to try for Leconfield again and to leave the 'secret mission' for somebody else to carry out.

We landed back in Hull about 2.30 p.m.and I was relieved to see that my car was still in one piece with its green light intact – most unusual. When my colleague parked his car in the same spot for a much shorter time a week later he returned to it to find only a neatly snipped wire on the roof. I have lost three flashing light units during my career, usually when I have parked in the University district of the city. I'm sure they finish up as disco lights in student accommodation.

As a result of that trip the pilot was awarded the Airforce Medal for Bravery, thoroughly deserved as the standard of flying had been quite brilliant. All I got out of it was a set of very smelly clothes and a huge sense of relief at being back home safely. My spirit of adventure seemed to be fading fast.

A trip we made to a Grimsby trawler did nothing to revive it. A diabetic crewman had gone into a coma down in the engine room and become trapped between the wall and a hot pipe. The only access was down a narrow steep companion ladder through a hatch some three and a half feet square. The engine room was quite dark and the winchman came down with me to hold a torch. The patient must have weighed about 17 stones and it was obvious that the only way we were going to get him out of there was to revive him so that he could climb out under his own steam. He had been unconscious for several hours and had burns to his arm where it was resting on the pipe and it was only with great difficulty that I managed to get an intravenous line into him. I had to give him three times the usual amount of sugar solution before he began to regain consciousness and when he did he became extremely violent – a classic result of this type of coma. He charged around the engine room after the winchman and myself, trying to throw us against the wall. As we scrambled away from him begging him to calm down we kept bumping into hot pipes and sharp bits of machinery. Fortunately he suddenly decided to go up the ladder and by the time he reached the deck he had made an almost complete recovery. He stood chatting to his mates while we staggered up after him and I proceeded to be very seasick for the first time in my helicopter career. The combination of the heat of the engine room, a Force 5 wind and sheer naked terror was too much for my stomach. The patient was most concerned and kept asking me if I was all right! The ironic thing was that it was entirely his own fault. The cause of his coma was a combination of his diabetes, an inadequate diet and the illegal consumption of alcohol.

The final straw came some seven weeks after my foggy experience and was again on a Sunday afternoon. The call-out was to a trawler on which a crewman had suffered a head injury the previous evening. The Master was very concerned because the man was still drowsy and was also vomiting and complaining of pain in his back and a severe headache. On the flight out the winchman told me that his previous trip had been a bit rough and he had dropped heavily onto the deck and hurt *his* back so he wouldn't be coming down with me that day, but he would be in control of my descent. Whether it was his back injury or not I don't know but I had a very bumpy ride, the strop of the support belt jerking my spine painfully several times on the way down.

The injured crewman had almost certainly been drinking when he had fallen down the ladder into the hold and was indeed still drunk. My anxiety was that he had suffered a fracture of the spine in the mid-thoracic region so we loaded him onto a Neil-Robertson stretcher, specially constructed for spinal injuries, and attempted to manoeuvre him up the narrow stairway out of the hold. It was very hard work and my already ill-treated back suffered even more. When we finally got him back to Hull he had a blood alcohol level of 230mgms so he certainly was still very drunk. No wonder he was vomiting and had a headache. At least he didn't need any anaesthetic!

All in all it was a bad trip and I decided that I was really getting too old for it. I had lost my enthusiasm for risking my life for people who should have known better and later that week I handed my flying suit over to a younger colleague. I haven't been up in a helicopter since.

CHILD ABUSE

The distressing facts about the abuse of children and my attempts to raise the profile of the problems involved in its recognition.

The abuse of children, physically, emotionally and sexually, is not a new problem as any reader of the scriptures will confirm. Medical writings are, however, quite recent. Apart from a brief reference in 1882 by Anthony Trollope they only really start in 1946 when Caffey, a Canadian Radiologist, noted a relationship between long bone fractures and subdural haematoma, writing a paper on the subject in the Canadian Journal of Radiology.

In 1962 Professor Kempe, Professor of Paediatrics in Denver, Colorado, alerted the world to the problem with his landmark article 'The Battered Baby Syndrome' in the Journal of the American Medical Association. The United Kingdom did not wake up to the fact that children here were as much at risk as they were in the United States until the Maria Colwell scandal in 1973. The seven year old girl had been wheeled into the Casualty Department of Brighton District General Hospital by her mother who said that she had 'just stopped breathing'. Even this tragedy would have gone largely unnoticed had it not been for the campaign waged by the tabloids, in particular the Daily Mirror, whose screaming headlines alerted the general public to the problem of child abuse.

On the whole the British public tends to adopt an ostrich-like attitude to the way children are treated within the confines of the family home and also assumes that if they are in care or fostered they must be being looked after properly. The famous British reticence and a horror of being thought 'nosy' combine to make us ignore what is going on often on our own doorstep. The attitude is that the way people bring up their children is their business. Up until the late nineteenth century children were expected to contribute to the family income by working up chimneys, down mines, on the land and in factories and sweat shops. Even the Education Act of 1882 which required all children under the age of 14 to attend school for at least two hours per day did little to protect them.

In 1886 a missionary working on the streets of New York befriended a neglected and dirty little waif called Mary Ellen and in the absence of any law in the USA to protect children (although there was one to protect animals!) enlisted the powers of a criminal justice lawyer in the Supreme Court of Justice on her behalf. Following this she founded the New York Society for the Prevention of Cruelty to Children. In 1889 the Reverend Agnew visited New York, was impressed by the work of the Society and on his return to England founded the Liverpool Society for the Prevention of Cruelty to Children in 1891, which was followed by a London branch and finally in 1892 amalgamated into the National organisation, the NSPCC, that everyone recognises today.

Fortunately, although my childhood was not without incident I was never abused in any way. I received the occasional smacked bottom which I'm sure was richly deserved but I had no personal experience to draw upon when in 1972, just before Maria Colwell's death and before any official guidelines had been drawn up by the Department of Health on how to handle such problems, I had to deal with a case of abuse myself. I was in General Practice in York at the time and running a regular mother and baby clinic every Wednesday afternoon with the help of the Practice Nurse, Eunice Mowett.

A young lady I hadn't seen before and who was not registered with me came to the clinic with her four month old baby boy. She asked if she could register with the Practice as she had recently moved locally from the other side of the city. She wanted me to have a look at her baby who had a painful arm which she said her previous GP had caused by giving him an immunisation injection two weeks previously which had made his arm become swollen and painful. She blamed the doctor for the way the injection had been given. After even a cursory examination I could see that the pain and swelling were nothing to do with the injection but were localised around the shoulder which was almost certainly broken. I decided to examine the baby more thoroughly all over as I had a feeling that things were definitely not right. As I removed his nappy I heard a sharp intake of breath from Nurse Mowett as she took a step back and noticed the sudden pallor of the baby's mother as she anticipated my reaction. I felt a sensation of total anger and disgust as I saw a deep incised wound across the top of the baby's penis. How, why, who, when, where? The questions flooded into my mind but before I had time to ask them the mother rushed to tell me how she had 'caught him with a safety pin' as she was changing his nappy before coming to the clinic.

It was the first of many such obvious lies I was to hear during the next twenty-five years. The explanation for what was clearly a cut with either a sharp knife or a razor blade was so blatantly untrue that I was amazed that the mother had even bothered to offer it. I remain surprised to this day by just what 'tall stories' are told to explain children's injuries.

Back in 1972 my horror was complete. How could anyone do such a thing to a helpless baby, unable to protect himself or to tell anyone about it? Many reasons are offered by parents as to why they harm their children, but in this case the mother was quite clearly severely emotionally disturbed and sad rather than bad. Adopted by an elderly couple she had led a very sheltered existence under very strict discipline and had few friends. On reaching her teens she had rebelled. Rebellion was the 'in' thing in the swinging sixties and early seventies and she had made a conscious decision to get herself pregnant, probably as a means of escape.

She had specifically wanted a little girl, maybe so that she could give her all the things she had never had, but life's not like that and her baby was a boy. Without family support she suffered severe post-natal depression leading to a psychotic condition in which she genuinely thought she could change the baby's sex by cutting off his penis. Deciding what ought to be done was not difficult. Actually implementing that decision when there were no guidelines laid down and very few colleagues with experience of such cases was a different matter. The answer was to set up a small multi-disciplinary group which would look after the welfare of both mother and child, not just immediately but long-term. That day was the start of my twenty-five years of involvement with Child Protection. My experiences during that time would fill several books, not just one chapter and would be out of place here but I would like to record just one or two cases which have had a great influence on me, changing my way of thinking and even my beliefs.

During my short stay in Blackpool I was requested by the Director of Public Health and Medicine to set up some guidelines for the management of child abuse in the Blackpool Health Authority's area. I owe a huge debt of gratitude to Malcolm Hall, a colleague in Preston, for assistance and advice. Along with Christine Cooper, Consultant Paediatrician in Newcastle, he was leading the way in raising the awareness of the enormity of the child abuse problem in the United Kingdom and was able to guide me not only in Child Protection issues but also in the early stages of my career in Accident and Emergency. It was his influence and that of another friend, Howard Baderman (who is still a Consultant in A & E at University College, London and still a trusty adviser in time of need) which were instrumental in my eventual return to Hull.

Mind you, most people who grow up in the city or spend their formative years here tend to return eventually, a reflection of the very introspective and parochial nature of the place. I have on occasion when I have been lecturing far afield referred to Hull as a 'little fishing village at the end of the A63' as it has more of the feel of that than of a huge international port. There are few places to compare with it. It is fiercely independent, this 'City and County of

Kingston upon Hull', steeped in history and tradition, and it has pulled itself up by its bootstraps from the devastation of the wartime blitz to be a thriving industrial centre and the 'Gateway to Europe'. However it also has a reputation for violence, crime, drunkenness, drug-taking and trafficking, and has the dubious distinction of having almost the highest recognised incidence of child abuse in the country. In 1975 I became acutely aware of this fact.

Only three months after I had taken up the post of Consultant in Charge of the Accident and Emergency Department at Hull Royal Infirmary, little Gary N was rushed in at 11.00 o'clock one morning with his mother shrieking that he had 'just stopped breathing'. She was clearly lying as rigor mortis had set in, he had multiple bruises all over his body and he was clothed in a pristine babygrow over a clean dry nappy. They came from a deprived area of the city and believe me, nobody comes from there in mid-morning, having supposedly been asleep all night, dressed in clean clothes and with a dry nappy. He had obviously been cleaned up specially for us but we weren't fooled. The official cause of death was a ruptured liver leading to Hypovolaemia due to a massive haemorrhage – he had lived just long enough to bruise. The perpetrator of the injuries was the mother's eighteen year old co-habitee.

Within the next few months I saw several other severely injured children and thought I was becoming quite an expert in recognising 'non-accidental injuries' until Michael E was brought in, this time at 1.00 o'clock on a Saturday afternoon. He was admitted to the A & E Department suffering from 40% scalds, with the explanation that he had pulled a kettle of boiling water over himself in the kitchen. This was confirmed by the ambulance driver who had seen the overturned kettle and the water on the floor. Michael was very ill and after resuscitation was transferred to the Regional Burns Unit at Pinderfields Hospital in Wakefield.

My reactions were purely clinical while I was treating him and the thought that the story was untrue never entered my head. It was only en-route to Wakefield that I noticed the bruising to his cheek and, more significantly, a bite mark on his forearm. I telephoned the Police from Pinderfields. How could I not have noticed the bruises and the bite mark? And now I thought about it the distribution of the scalding was more consistent with him being dipped in boiling water rather than with him tipping it over himself. The fact is that at times it was beyond my comprehension that anyone could do anything so horrendous to a defenceless child, but I was learning rapidly. I had to.

Case after case came through the doors of HRI and it wasn't long before a system of referral was set up in the city and a request made that all suspected victims of non-accidental injury be examined by a paediatrician. Doctors Phillpot and Pugh were not altogether pleased. By nature they were kind caring doctors who devoted their lives to making sick children better. Their involvement in the field of forensic pathology with the inevitable round of meetings with police and social workers, often leading to appearances as witnesses in both Civil and Criminal Courts was anathema to them, but it would have been worth it in the long run. However they were more than happy to leave it to me.

I have to admit that to me the whole thing was a huge challenge and the start of a crusade which, as I have said, was to last for twenty-five years. It can only be compared to an unending ride on a rollercoaster - there were always to be higher peaks and deeper troughs ahead.

By this time I had already met M several times, as indeed had my predecessor and, more importantly, Dr Bickford, Medical Superintendent of the De La Pole Psychiatric Hospital which was situated in Cottingham on the western outskirts of Hull. Mavis was one of twins who in her early teens had started to present herself to various agencies with different types and degrees of self-abuse. She deliberately overdosed, repeatedly slashed her arms and her abdomen and stuck sharp objects such as needles, pieces of metal and broken glass into herself. She also swallowed a variety of things with the potential to do her serious harm. Why she did it was a complete mystery. She clearly had extremely low self-esteem and wanted to draw attention to herself and for some reason she wanted us to be involved. She never intentionally put her life seriously at risk, although sometimes she came perilously close, usually by accident. She was a psychopath who refused to learn. She involved a large number of people who all tried to help her but to no avail and I got to know her quite well without understanding her at all.

Then she announced that she was pregnant! A group of people who had been involved with the care of M over several years met, discussed the situation and agreed that it would be entirely inappropriate for her to keep the baby and that it should be taken into care at birth. There were several reasons. M was mentally ill, her behaviour was so anti-social that she could not possibly care for a child, and she did not reach my own bench-mark, which I adhere to to this day, that a prospective parent must be capable of exhibiting 'good enough' parenting skills, which M patently did not.

When little Sheila was born she was placed immediately with foster parents and M returned to her pattern of self-abuse with increased intensity. Then about ten months later she turned up in the Department dressed up as

130

usual in leather trousers, leather jacket adorned with a variety of badges and stickers and a cowboy hat and boots. She hadn't overdosed and didn't seem to be injured in any way but asked to see me. By now she was twenty-six, but behaved more like a fourteen year old. "I'm pregnant again," she told me. And she was, this time with twins. The whole process was repeated and the twin girls were duly fostered at birth.

Why do people foster children? Why do people choose to work with children, seek employment in children's homes, devote their lives to looking after young people? It is hard and often unrewarding, even heartbreaking work. Ninety-nine percent of the time it is because they genuinely love children and young people and because it fulfils a need in them - a need to be needed. Sadly in the remaining one percent it is for other, twisted, reasons and these people are past masters in the art of dissembling as many recent cases show.

The three children were all made Wards of Court and M had no right of access to any of them. After the birth of the twins the frequency of her self-abuse rose again. Then quite suddenly it stopped. She got married, became pregnant and as her husband was not known to the authorities for any reason their baby son, Martin, was allowed to stay with them. He was, however, also made a Ward of Court and placed on the 'At Risk' register. M was given considerable support by the Local authority in caring for the child by way of Day Care, classes in Parenting Skills and home visits. I saw her less frequently and hoped that all was well.

One day in early February, when the temperature was well below zero, a Care Assistant went to collect Martin from home to take him to the Day Centre. There was no answer to her knock and the door was locked but she could hear Martin crying. The social worker and the police were called and they broke in and found Martin in his bedroom dressed only in a T-shirt and shorts and a very wet nappy. The temperature inside the house was four degrees centigrade and he was very cold and hungry. They brought him into the Department where we gave him quantities of warm fluids and he demolished an entire packet of digestive biscuits. Then he sat absolutely still and quiet, exhibiting the classic symptoms of 'frozen awareness'. He was also suffering physically from exposure to extreme cold with frost-bitten toes on both feet. A Judge had no hesitation in implementing the 'Ward of Court' powers and handing him over to the care of the Local Authority. His Mother's parenting skills were obviously still not 'good enough'.

So what of her other children? As I said, the twins had been placed with foster parents at birth by the Local Authority, which should have ensured that

131

their welfare and security were safeguarded, but by the age of four they were both displaying bizarre behaviour traits. By the time they started school they were clearly behind in their development. They then started to display more sinister symptoms, indicative of sexual abuse, and were removed from their foster home and placed in a Local Authority home where they were cared for by a highly skilled lady who specialised in the care of sexually abused children.

After about three months I was asked to examine them for physical signs of abuse in order to decide whether a legal investigation into their foster care was necessary. At that time we were using 'anatomically correct' dolls in diagnostic work - a procedure not generally accepted as being accurate enough to use in court nowadays as it is construed as being misleading. Prior to a physical examination of the girls, during the course of winning their confidence, we were using the 'father' doll with Sarah when she became very angry, tore off its clothes, ran to the door, opened it and flung the now naked doll across the waiting room. It landed on the lap of a parent waiting for an appointment with one of my colleagues. With as much dignity as I could muster I walked across, requested the return of the doll and walked back into the consulting room, closing the door firmly behind me!

Sadly a physical examination later confirmed that both little girls had been grossly and repeatedly sexually abused, both vaginally and anally. I remain convinced that the sign of 'Reflex Anal Dilation' is strong and incontrovertible evidence of sexual abuse when looked at in conjunction with behavioural and verbal evidence. The diagnosing of sexual abuse became the subject of intense debate during the 'Cleveland Inquiry' when the physical signs of abuse were contested by many medical experts. Perhaps the word 'expertise' should be replaced by experience. The experience of doctors who have spent many hours talking to abused children and at the same time looking for physical signs should be acknowledged. After twenty-five years of working closely with abused children I am certain that observation should be made of the whole child, not just isolated physical signs or verbal testimony. Only when behaviour, physical signs and verbal testimony all point to abuse does the evidence become 'safe'. The twin girls convinced me of this all those years ago and I have seen nothing since to make me change my mind. I haven't seen any of those children for more than ten years now and, despite their bad beginning, I hope they are leading as normal a life as possible. I did however see M again under quite extraordinary circumstances and in order to arrive at that meeting I must retrace my steps a little.

There is a saying that true friends can be counted on the fingers of one hand, acquaintances need many. David was one such 'true friend'. I first met him when I came back to Hull and my first wife worked as a nurse at Frances Askew School where my father had taught many years before and where David was a teacher. He was, to all intents and purposes, "Mr Gipsyville". Most of the children in the area had been or were being taught by him, most of the boys had played football for his team and most of the parents acknowledged his influence on their children's lives. His working day was never 9 till 4. He always stayed on after school to run clubs and societies or coach football and spent much of his holidays introducing his pupils to the delights of Yorkshire's coast and moorland.

He was a confirmed bachelor, an obsessive fisherman, a collector of bizarre antiquities, kept rabbits and rats and played a mean game of snooker, a sport he introduced me to. He was considered by many people who didn't really know him to be a complete oddball. Maybe he was, but he was a very special oddball. He was a man of high principles and totally reliable. If he said he would do something he would do it, come hell or high water. In twenty years of friendship he never once let me down. I doubt if he could have said the same about me.

He believed in no specific god, didn't recognise birthdays or Christmas and when I asked him to be Godfather to my youngest daughter, Rebecca, he refused. He did, however, turn up at the Christening and courteously and carefully explained to the priest why he could not accept, then proceeded to act more like a Godparent for the rest of his all-too-short life than any of the official ones.

Games were for winning, not just taking part in. I never beat him at chess or for that matter at any board game and our snooker battles turned into a life-long war. Our local snooker club witnessed an epic stalemate between the two of us, neither of us willing to give way until the club chairman finally called a halt to it as it was obviously never going to be resolved. It was the only time we ever played against each other in competition and when the frame was restarted I managed to win. I don't think David ever quite got over it.

Perhaps most sacred to David was our professional relationship. Over the years quite a few of the children he taught became my patients, either as a result of accidents or abuse, but he never sought to discuss them with me, and although I would gladly have given it he never asked me for medical advice for himself. Not, that is, until it was too late.

It was soon after Kathleen and I had set up home together in Goddard Avenue. He had consulted his GP about a lump in his neck and had been prescribed antibiotics. He asked me what I thought. What he thought was that he had cancer and what he was really saying was 'What can I do and will you help me?' It wasn't just immediate help he was asking for, it was long term.

I felt his neck. He had secondary tumours which had developed so rapidly that the prognosis was dreadful. I realised that I had no alternative but to tell him the truth. Yes, he had cancer and it was very advanced. I referred him to one of my colleagues and we then entered a very different phase of our friendship. It was based on absolute honesty and total trust. He was not afraid of death, as neither indeed am I. He just wanted me to help him sort things out and help him enjoy his remaining months to the best of his (and my) ability. He wanted to get on with the business of dying with the minimum interference to his daily life.

Eventually, of course, this wasn't possible. It hurt him to have to stop playing football with his lads, to have to give up teaching, to stop going to the snooker club, but what hurt him most of all was becoming dependent on other people. He managed it with immense dignity and I felt a massive sense of pride to be allowed to be part of the life of a man who had done so much for so many people without expecting or wanting any recognition.

David had met Susan and her two daughters before his cancer was diagnosed and had decided to relinquish his bachelor status as soon as he was able. Then all his plans had to be put on hold. Susan, knowing he had only months to live, married him on Christmas Eve quietly at home with myself as witness. I have never been so deeply moved by the commitment of one human being to another. He had promised to come to my marriage to Kathleen and to act as my best man despite my repeated assurances that I would never get married again. When we had moved to Goddard Avenue we were both determined that there would be no wedding bells and that this would be our last move. David didn't believe us and frequently said that not only would we marry but that he didn't think we would stay in that house for more than a year or two. He was of course right on both counts and did in fact come to our wedding but was not alive to see our move to Lelley, although I'm sure he was aware of it!

It was when David was in hospital for the final time that I met M again. After a long struggle, with several remissions and periods of hope, David eventually had to submit to permanent hospitalisation in order to die with dignity and I visited him on a daily basis. When I was leaving the ward after one visit a staff nurse asked me if I knew a M D. She was on the ward and had been talking about me. It was indeed that same self-abusing M. She had been admitted with pneumonia the previous day. She had had no visitors so I went and talked to her for a while, then visited her each day for the next four or five days after I had seen David.

It was M who brought up the subject of her children uttering the unforgettable words, "You know Dr Gosnold you were right. There was no way I could have looked after those kids properly. At least I know they have good homes and are being cared for." She clearly had no idea what had happened to the twins and as far as I know she still doesn't. On her locker were three small photographs, all a bit creased and in cheap frames, one of her eldest daughter, one of the twins and one of Michael. She made constant reference to them, saying that every night she said a little prayer, asking that they be kept safe and thanking the kind people for looking after them. "I do love them, Dr Gosnold," she said.

M was one of life's sad people who had nothing going for them right from infancy, but she left hospital cured at least in body if not in mind. David, who had so much to offer to others, never did. He died peacefully in his sleep five hours after I had made an evening visit that we both knew would be the last. We had said our goodbyes and he had thanked me for being his friend. The privilege had been mine.

On the hallowed Wembley turf.

Roger 'the Dodger' Millward, the Hull KR Coach climbs aboard the coach to Wembley for the cup final against his old club: Castleford.

The band plays on before the massed crowds of the Hull KR and Castleford supporters.

EXTRA TIME

The spin-off from being a member of the medical profession as I am invited into the diverse worlds of Rugby League, BBC Radio and Police work..

Snooker wasn't the only outside activity in my busy life. Sport had always been important to me and in the 1970s I was to be given a chance to combine it with my medical career. At school and university I had played Rugby Union and although there were some excellent Union teams in the East Riding of Yorkshire, Hull itself was a stronghold of Rugby League with two teams, Hull and Hull Kingston Rovers, who in the past had always been there or thereabouts when the trophies were being handed out. But by 1976 when someone called Mike Page invited me to go along and watch Hull play Doncaster the great days were just a memory. Average home crowds were officially 3,860 but there were only 926 hardy souls scattered around Hull's Boulevard ground off Anlaby Road, not far from the hospital, on that bleak Sunday afternoon. It was only the second League game I had ever watched – at that time there was a good deal of snobbery between the two codes.

Exactly how Mike Page came to contact me was, and has remained, a mystery. I had been Consultant in Charge of the Accident and Emergency Unit for only a few months although I was, of course, a local lad. Mike had played cricket for Derbyshire and was currently an enthusiastic member of the Board of the ailing Hull RLFC, with little or no support from Chairman Charlie Watson or Secretary Peter Darley, but with an up-and-coming Roy Waudby on the sidelines. The team captain was Brian Hancock.

Mike was a worker, outspoken in support of the club's supporters and a bit of a rebel. He always made a point of watching home games from the 'Threepenny Stand' rather than the Directors' box. I had no choice but to stand there with him on that cold damp afternoon, sleet driving into our faces, our shoes soaking with the urine which always trickled down from the back. To our right was the scoreboard – a depressing sight – and the almost empty Gordon Street Terraces. To our left the Airlie Street end was as usual rather better populated because it afforded some protection from the prevailing wind. Airlie Street also gave the team its nickname, the Airlie Birds. Because of the idiosyncrasies of the unique Hull accent this became the Airlie Bairds - or Early Birds in anybody else's language. But I digress.

The majority of the spectators were either with us under the cover of the Threepenny Stand or in the East Stand opposite where the Directors' box also had its lofty perch. The whole place had an air of having seen better days and the mood of the crowd matched the surroundings. The only other time I had watched Hull play was in the late 1950s when the likes of Johnny Whitely, the Drake twins and Cyril Sykes were household names. I roused myself from these gloomy thoughts when I realised Mike was talking to me.

"How about it then John? Do you want to join us? Be the Airlie Birds club doctor? Come to Wembley with us?"

'Dream on,' I thought. However, although the club might have been ailing, the welcome I received after the match was great, the hospitality superb despite the disastrous lack of facilities and I agreed to give it a go.

I soon discovered that there were some bad medical practices in place both during matches and in training which I insisted must be changed immediately. Training was poorly organised, with repetitive work that often did more harm than good, and many of the players were carrying chronic injuries. They were not full-time 'professionals' as they are now and often spent all day working at a physically demanding job before attending training three or four evenings a week. Conflict between coach and players was never far away and when David Doyle-Davidson was replaced by Arthur Bunting it boiled over.

The magical 'steroid jab' had until then been the panacea for all ills – 'just gie 'im a shot o' steroids doc - 'e'll be all right.' But the trouble lay in the fact that they ignored any advice that it should be followed by rest, then progressive rehabilitation of the injured joint if they were not to finish up with a chronic condition and an even longer period of unavailability. They couldn't afford to stay off work and were afraid they would lose their place in the team if they were absent for long. I managed to effect a gradual change in attitude, but only slowly. One thing that did surprise me was that however non-sterile the conditions in which I had to sew up a wound I cannot recall any subsequent infections. Obviously I always used all possible means available to prevent contamination - exploring the wound and removing grass, gravel, even glass and any other debris, and spraying the wound with Disadine DP (Povidine Iodine, a powerful antiseptic) both before and after closure, but I would have expected some infection, especially as the patients subsequently played on. I put it down to the fact that the time lapse between the damage being caused and the closing of the wound was never more than ten minutes and it became clear that sitting in a hospital waiting room for hours on end with an open wound allowed contamination with resistant bacteria.

One of the greatest battles I had to fight was to ensure that the whole squad had prophylactic anti-tetanus injections before the season started. I waged a battle of a different kind with the Board of Directors, trying to persuade them that before signing, new players should have to undergo a thorough medical examination, even such luminaries as the great Steve 'Knocker' Norton and Vince Farrar from Castleford and Charlie Stone from Featherstone, who all joined the club in 1977 when the scrum was being rebuilt. Also by then, as with other clubs, overseas players were being wooed, especially from Australia and New Zealand and Dane O'Hara, Gary Kemble and James Leuleui exchanged the sunshine of down under for the chill of East Yorkshire.

Dane O'Hara's first game at the Boulevard was memorable for the fact that he received a heavy blow to the chest and I diagnosed my first and only traumatic pneumothorax on a Rugby League field. It occurs when air leaks into the chest cavity causing pressure on the lungs, which can lead to their collapse and unless treated promptly the patient virtually suffocates. Fortunately we were close to the hospital and a confirmatory Xray, a local anaesthetic and a chest drain soon solved the problem and he was back in training within a few weeks.

The late '70s saw a great deal of hard work by coach and squad and gradually the team's fortunes began to revive. Games were won with increasing frequency but the club still lacked a reliable kicker to convert the tries and benefit from penalties. That was when Sammy Lloyd arrived. He quickly established his reputation by beating the club record for points scored in a season held since 1956 by Colin Hutton. During the 1978 season Sammy kicked 170 goals and scored a total of 369 points. The team won all twenty-six of their league matches. No-one who was privileged to be at the Challenge Cup semi-final against Widnes at Swinton in 1980 will ever forget his magnificent kick from the touchline in the last minute of the match which earned them a place in the final against arch-rivals Hull Kingston Rovers, known as the Robins because of their red and white strip.

Hull KR were based in East Hull and were led at that time by player-manager Roger Milward, arguably the greatest scrum half in the history of the game. Hull FC, who played in black and white, had never won a Challenge Cup Final at Wembley and things were not about to change. Indeed as I write, nearly twenty years later, they still have not achieved that ambition and are certainly not fancied to do so at the moment. That final in 1980 has to be one of the most memorable occasions in Rugby League history. Whatever the outcome a Hull team would win and the city went wild. Although British Rail put on separate trains for the rival fans they defied segregation and piled into the first one they saw. In any case loyalties were often divided within families, husbands and wives sticking by the team they had supported before they were married, but the rivalry was friendly and the whole day was good-humoured.

As well as those travelling by rail fans poured out of Hull in cars, red and white and black and white scarves streaming from the windows as they travelled in convoy along Boothferry Road, the main route out of the city to the west. At the boundary someone had attached a large sign to a lamp post on the side of the road - 'Last one out put out the light'. To be involved was a fabulous experience, and Mike Page reminded me of his original promise.

We had a good team and deserved to be favourites. Our preparation had been meticulous and as the luxury coach left for a hotel in Hendon - dubbed the 'Hendon Hideaway' - team spirit and camaraderie were steadily and skillfully built. I learned how nerves can play such an important part in recovery from injury and how 'prima donnas' develop 'a bit of a muscle pull doc' at crucial moments. The physiotherapy room was always full by then, but I had tried in vain to persuade the team coach to adopt a modern approach to the game as far as diet was concerned. I had talked at length to Arthur Bunting about the American regime of protein, protein and more protein during the two weeks leading up to an important match, then pure carbohydrate for the final twenty-four hours, but he thought it was a load of clap-trap. Some of the players took notice and I am sure that on the day they did have more energy and stamina and were better prepared than those who, like Mike Crane, stuck to their normal diet of chips, beer and cigarettes. Having said that, all the players were remarkably fit for part-time sportsmen and certainly had a professional approach to the game. I have fond memories of joining in with training sessions as I was also quite fit in those days and I still have my number 15 jersey, given to me by the team as a souvenir of the day when I was a potential substitute!

Memories of the day itself are somewhat blurred, but I retain an impression of the coach trip up Wembley Way to the famous stadium through the cheering crowds of fans, being allowed to walk onto the actual pitch with the team before the match, pulling Sammy Lloyd's leg when he missed a practice kick at goal (not nearly as significant as the one he missed during the match itself) and the surprisingly old fashioned dressing rooms. Then there was the nerve-wracking wait in the tunnel exchanging banter with Hull KR's team doctor, Stuart Lunt, listening to the crowd singing 'Abide With Me', then walking forward in the silence. As you walk up the slight incline there is a square in front of you like a kaleidoscope, filled with light and shifting colour from the other side of the ground, but there is very little noise. Then as you step out into the sunlight the roar hits you like a physical blow and legs can buckle as the nerves take over. That year the occasion was graced by the Queen Mother. Before we had gone out onto the field we had been reminded by a royal equerry that she was tiny and quite frail and that a handshake from the beefy mauler of a seventeen stone rugby player could be damaging unless care was taken! As ever the Queen Mum was delightful and gracious, wittily apt with her comments, and I enjoyed my brief encounter with royalty.

The game itself was over before it really began. The Airlie Birds were defeated - the outcome of a long war rather than a great battle. Roger Milward will certainly remember it for ever, not just because the Robins won but because he had his jaw broken in several places and Steve Hubbard was stretchered off with a broken ankle. Our team sustained no physical injuries - indeed they hardly seemed to exert themselves. They lost 10-5 in a dour and disappointingly undistinguished match.

After that season my relationship with team coach Arthur Bunting and with Roy Waudby, who had by then taken over as Chairman of the Board, deteriorated and the fun went out of the game as far as I was concerned. I had only ever been in it for the fun - certainly not for the money - and we eventually parted company. I was still with them when they drew with Widnes in 1981 but when they lost 14-12 to Featherstone Rovers in 1983 as the result of a late penalty I was just an ordinary spectator, not the team doctor.

I had no intention of ever becoming involved with Rugby League again, but in 1984 I received a telephone call from Roger Milward asking whether I fancied joining the opposition! Roger was a very different kettle of fish from Arthur Bunting. Having retired as a player he had stayed on at the club to share the coaching of the first team with Jed Dunn and I had the privilege of witnessing and sharing in his professional approach. He was a real motivator, with first hand experience of the game, and was respected by the players. Never once in my association with Hull KR did he ask me to do anything he knew I would disagree with. If I said a player was unfit he accepted that he was unfit and all he asked was when he would be ready to resume training. On match days it was a different ball game. He would get through forty or fifty cigarettes and I'm sure he was really a total neurotic who needed to live close to the edge. However to watch him in action as he prepared the team for a game was an absolute delight. I would like to be able to quote at length from his team talks to the players both before the start and at half-time, especially if they were losing, but his liberal use of four-letter words makes it impractical. It was certainly effective and no doubt the kind of language the majority of his team were quite used to. I stood by with respectful and admiring astonishment. It was a different world.

In 1985 we were off to Wembley again when the Robins played Roger's old team Castleford. That was where he had been born and bred and had never really left, commuting over to Hull from the West Riding nearly every day. Sadly I was yet again on the losing side and I will never forget Roger's heartfelt words to me as we walked back to the dressing-room after the match. "John - you're just a f****** Jonah!" I believe I am still the only medic in the history of Rugby League to have been to Wembley as team doctor for two different losing sides!

Memories of that cup final which have stayed with me are of working in the shadow of Windsor Castle in the week prior to the match to try to get George Fairburn's knee into shape for what was likely to be his last important match and in the process twisting my own knee, rendering me first immobile, then only able to walk with a pronounced limp. During the match itself my hamstring gave way completely and television viewers were treated to the sight of me struggling painfully across the famous Wembley turf and my 'funny walk' as I tried to assist the stretcher bearers as they carried the not inconsiderable weight of the injured Gavin Miller off the pitch.

By the early 1990s the character of Rugby League began to change. Big money was injected into one or two elite clubs and the game began to lose its universal appeal and the following it had built up amongst television viewers courtesy of the inimitable commentator Eddie Waring. Roger Milward left Hull KR and George Fairburn took over a somewhat depleted and inexperienced squad. He did remarkably well with them and I stayed with him for three years but neither of us got on particularly well with Phil Lowe who had taken over from Colin Hutton as Chairman. When George left in 1994 I left as well, only to be invited by Hull Rugby Union Football Club to help them out. It was like returning home. The team was an amalgamation of the old Hull and East Riding RUFC who had shared the Circle on Anlaby Road with Hull Cricket Club, and the Old Hymerians, the old boys team from my former school.

They played at the latter's ground, Haworth Park, and memories of school cross-country runs flooded back. I had hated long-distance running. I was by nature and build a sprinter and vividly remember to this day setting off from Haworth Park, across the field and up onto the bank of the River Hull. I would contrive in every possible way to cut corners and shorten the six miles to the finish. I would mutter darkly that I was a sprinter, not a ruddy marathon runner and that if I had been born in Russia I would have had a muscle biopsy at birth and then been trained as a sprinter, harnessing the potential of my white muscle fibres and not my red ones and that I should never be expected to run more than 400 metres! The P E master quite rightly took no notice of this pretentious rubbish and told me to get on with it, but my sprinting ability did take me into both school and university rugby teams and, as my medical career progressed, assisted my understanding of sports injuries. Now I was back on home ground. The wheel had turned full circle.

Quite different was my job as Police Surgeon to the Humberside Police Force. I had been encouraged to take the post by Philip Science, who was Coroner at the time of the Wensley Lodge fire. Then John Shores, with whom I had become friendly after helping him out with the odd GP surgery, invited me to join him, Percy Scott and Geoffrey Staley to become an Assistant Police Surgeon.

Not only has its name now changed to 'Forensic Medical Examiner' but the whole job has changed. When I started twenty years ago the bulk of the work was drink/driving blood tests, checking on prisoners locked up in the cells who were often drunk but otherwise usually quite fit and examining victims of assault or rape. My involvement in child protection was also in fact part of a Police Surgeon's job. To describe all the incidents with which I have been involved would fill another book or two, but it is worth recounting one or two individual cases to illustrate the changes in the nature of the work. This is partly due to the fact that Policing itself has changed. In the 'old days' there were officers like Sergeant Brian Sargent who knew his patch so well that he could almost forecast when a member of the Hessle Road community was going to commit a felony, let alone sort it out when it had happened. Now the local bobby is often a much more remote person, usually ensconced behind the wheel of a car rather than walking the beat and the role of the CID is being seriously eroded. The job is more stereotyped and involved with paperwork rather than allowing for a flamboyant and individual method of policing. All this must be causing my late good friend and mentor John Rose, who was Chief Superintendent CID until he retired, to turn in his grave.

When I started, the job of Charge-room Sergeant was busy but not nearly as stressful and responsible as it is today with the introduction of PACE, the Police and Criminal Evidence Bill. The increased accountability and the increase in the number of quite ill prisoners suffering from the effects of a variety of drugs taken in excess and often in 'cocktails' makes the job very hazardous. Deaths in Custody are no longer a rarity and are usually due to self-inflicted illness by the prisoner rather than the police brutality so often alleged. Twenty years ago it was rare for me to have to attend a prisoner suffering from the effects of drugs. When I did it was usually the misuse of amphetamines. Now nearly every prisoner seems to be high on either Heroin, Methadone or Benzodiazapine, or drunk on extra strong beer or cider. There has been a dramatic change in the habits of both the criminal fraternity and society in general.

There has also been a change in the methods used for suicide and an increase in its frequency. Overdoses in the main used to involve barbiturates, now it is more often a combination of Paracetamol and Dextropopoxythene. One memorable suicide I had to attend was that of a hanging in Hull prison when I had to confirm the death of a young man whom I had earlier seen in the A&E Department of Hull Royal when the young son of his girlfriend had been 'brought in dead'. 'Wayne' had been dead for several hours by the time his mother carried him into the hospital, screaming hysterically that he had 'just stopped breathing'. He had rigor mortis, a fractured skull and rope marks round his wrists where his arms had been tied together in his cot. Both his big toe nails were missing, pulled off by the mother's co-habitee while in a drugged state. Every member of staff on duty that day was extremely distressed by the sight of that poor little boy who had been tortured and murdered and I cried unashamedly when I had to show him to his maternal grandmother who had to officially identify him, as his parents had been taken into custody. It was several days later when I saw the co-habitee again in Hull prison where he had been on remand. I must admit that I had quite different feelings about his death than I had at his son's.

Sometimes people 'hang' themselves by accident and one of my duties was to advise the investigating officer when a man had suffered accidental death during sexual gratification. The sight of a man dressed in female attire and surrounded by the paraphernalia of sexual aids, pornographic magazines and videos and other bizarre tools of sexual deviation is quite distressing. Examinations of people who have been assaulted are also very upsetting as, however sympathetically they are carried out, they are degrading to the victims, adding insult to injury. The most memorable of these was the case of an educationally sub-normal young lady whom I had to examine after she had made allegations of 'rape' against a man whom she knew quite well. Many rapes are perpetrated by someone who is known by the complainant. On this occasion I was struck by the lack of intelligence of the girl and her inability to describe any details of the assault. She just complained about the alleged rapist and 'the dog in the room' with him. I was also perplexed by the mud on her inner thighs and an extremely profuse amount of secretion in her upper vagina. When the pathologist's report came back several days later raising the possibility of the secretions being 'of canine origin' the significance of 'the dog in the room' became clear.

Forensic Medical work is interesting, challenging, confronts the often brutal realities of life and provides useful extra money to pay for holidays! On

145

the down side it plays havoc with sleep and off-duty time.

Another 'spin-off' from my professional life was my involvement with BBC Radio Humberside, one of the earliest and most successful Local Radio stations in the country. I had often been asked to take part in programmes in my role as A&E Consultant and had enjoyed broadcasting. As a result of this I was invited to join the station's Local Radio Advisory Council, a body of listeners who monitor the output and meet regularly with senior management to offer criticism, praise and suggestions and to review individual programmes in depth. From 1989 to 1993 I was Chairman of this committee and also a member of the wider ranging BBC Northern Regional Advisory Council.

To celebrate its 10th birthday BBC Radio Humberside had invited listeners to join the present and former staff on a trip to the Continent. Hull is uniquely placed for such jaunts to Holland and Belgium as North Sea Ferries operates a nightly service to Rotterdam and Zeebrugge. The plan was to make a block booking on the ferry on a Friday evening, one night in a hotel or hotels and return overnight on Sunday, so offering a very reasonably priced weekend with everything laid on. It was a huge success, loyal listeners welcoming the chance to spend two whole days with the people they listened to every day but seldom saw, and it became an annual event. Destinations varied - Rotterdam, Amsterdam, Bruges, Brussels, even Arnhem and Paris. Hundreds of listeners from both north and south of the Humber eagerly looked forward to it. All needs were catered for and on-board entertainment became a tradition. The one thing lacking was a 'team doctor'.

With my arrival on the Advisory Council that problem was solved. Thinking about it this could have been a deep-laid plot by the then station manager Geoff Sargieson! Whatever, I was invited to accompany staff and listeners on that year's trip to The Hague as a guest - no strings attached, nothing to do, just enjoy the trip and get to know some of the Radio Humberside 'family'. It didn't quite work out like that however. As we were boarding an elderly man tripped and collapsed in front of me as we were going up the gangway. He had suffered a cardiac arrest and as there were no emergency medical facilities available the only recourse was mouth to mouth resuscitation, at which point it became nauseatingly obvious that he had had a pre-voyage drink or two! Sadly we failed to revive him and had to carry him back through customs and immigration - not without its bureaucratic problems and delaying the departure of the ferry. The other elderly gentleman he was travelling with decided that his friend wouldn't have wanted him to be disappointed so carried on with his weekend break! Fortunately he kept quiet

146

about the incident as one essential in times of crisis like this is not to spread alarm and despondency amongst the other passengers. When we finally got back on board I headed for the bar for a restorative drink, whereupon a man fell off his stool and dislocated his knee. Two down, one to go?

Arriving in the Hague we booked into our hotel, had dinner and retired for the night, commenting to each other that I was certainly earning my keep. In the early hours of the morning I was woken by a knock on the door. Could I please assist the local police? One of our party was sleep-walking in her nightdress through the streets. Could I clarify whether she was suffering from any mental illness? The following day there was an outbreak of diarrhoea and sickness amongst about twenty of the guests who had obviously eaten - or drunk - more well than wisely, and some of them were quite ill. On the way back to the ferry on Sunday we called in for lunch at Scheveningen, Holland's equivalent of Brighton, and one look at the sea made me realise that we were in for a rough ride home. The North Sea in February can be very inhospitable. About a hundred travellers were sea-sick and by the time I staggered off the ship on Monday morning I was shattered. Yes Geoff, thank you, for a lovely relaxing weekend.

On the grounds that this had never happened before and was unlikely to do so again I agreed to join the trip the following year. I must have been mad. At 3.00 a.m. there was a quiet knock on the cabin door. Trying not to wake Kathleen I crept out of my bunk and was escorted to the medical room where the purser was worried about an 18 year old female crew member who suffered from asthma. He was right to be worried. She was in extremis, gasping for breath, her respiration very shallow, deeply cyanosed, her pulse rate way up at about 160 beats per minute and virtually no recordable blood pressure. She was very ill indeed. So what emergency medical equipment was available? Well plenty of oxygen thank goodness, some Aminophylline, which opens up the bronchioles allowing air to get into the lungs, and some hydrocortisone which has an anti-inflammatory and anti-allergic effect to counteract the allergic reaction which sometimes triggers an asthma attack. Unfortunately there was no adrenaline and no ventilating equipment. More by luck than judgement I managed to keep her alive until we docked in Rotterdam and could accompany the Flying Squad who met the ship and took us to the local hospital intensive care unit. Since then North Sea Ferries, along with other ferry companies, have instituted first aid training programmes for their staff and installed emergency equipment on board. In addition the Hull company has a ship-to-shore direct radio link with the A&E Department of Hull Royal Infirmary. Happily the patient survived and a grateful ferry company rewarded me with a free trip to the Continent for the two of us plus our car!

No such reward from the BBC, just an invitation to join them again the next year when the return trip was dogged by apalling weather. It had become traditional that as the ferry neared the Humberside coast the early morning programme was broadcast live from the dining room of the ship. The presenter that year was Charlie Partridge, not the best of sailors. The Captain had run with the wind - a Force 11 gale - for as long as he could but eventually had to make a turn for the coast. As he turned and we hit the huge seas broadside on, every tea and coffee urn, every vat of orange juice and all the crockery and cutlery crashed to the floor. Charlie turned an interesting shade of green and Dave Taviner had to be shaken awake and told, in true thespian tradition, 'You're on!'

On another occasion when we had also had a rough crossing we were told as we neared Hull that there was a problem. The lock gates at King George Dock had been damaged in the storm and we couldn't dock. There was no other suitable berth for the huge ship so we turned right and spent the rest of the day cruising up and down off the coast of North East Yorkshire between Spurn Point and Flamborough Head. We knew exactly where we were by listening to Radio Humberside news bulletins, as listeners kept ringing in to the station to say they could see the unusual sight of a large passenger ship off Withernsea, or Hornsea or Bridlington. The Radio Humberside staff, led by the amiable disc jockey Steve Massam did their best to keep everyone happy, organising a quiz and an excellent sing-along accompanied on the piano by the station's resident organist Arnold Loxam who, fortuitously, was travelling with us. There were requests for such popular songs as 'Tulips from Amsterdam', 'We are Sailing' and "I Do Like to be Beside the Seaside'! Meanwhile the ship's crew kept us supplied with food and drink.

It proved impossible to repair the lock gates quickly and a decision was taken to dock at Immingham, across the river from Hull. Unfortunately there were no facilities there to deal with such a large number of passengers and immigration and customs officials had to come on board to process them. Long queues of by now very weary people had to wait on narrow stairways then stand in crowded corridors for hours. The ship was, of course, carrying normal passengers with cars as well as the Radio Humberside party and the usual quota of huge lorries. It was soon discovered that the exit ramp didn't match the dockside in height, so steel plates had to be welded to its end in order to discharge both vehicles and passengers. Although Radio Humberside had laid on a fleet of coaches to return its listeners to Hull, at such short notice and late at night it was anything but a luxury fleet and to add to the problems it was by now snowing heavily and the Humber Bridge had been closed because of the gales. On our coach Steve Massam eventually moved up to sit next to the driver and politely asked whether he could help by clearing the steam from the window as the heating wasn't working and the demister certainly wasn't demisting! It was a slow and wearisome trip all the way round by Goole and over the old Boothferry Bridge to retrieve our cars from the dockside in Hull.

Despite all this the weekends continued to be popular and I went on several more even after I had finished my stint on the Advisory Council. The one good thing to come out of them was a discussion with Margaret Garbett during one voyage about the possibility of collaborating on this book - and here we are!

The Norsun about to leave for another Radio Humberside trip to Holland.

A 'happy' Dr Gosnold with Tammy Cline enjoying the homeward-bound after-dinner entertainment.

Steve Massam and Judi Murden represent the Radio Station at a reception in Germany.

Geoff Sargieson's 50th! A collection of well-known rascals resting by the cross in Leyburn.

HOLIDAYS

Is there a doctor in the house - or on the plane - beach - motorway? Why me?

There are times when even doctors need to take a break, despite protests from their patients or staff and I have been lucky in being able to combine work with pleasure on many occasions when lecturing or attending conferences in exotic locations. More of that later, but sometimes we plan holidays that are just – well – holidays. Nice place, warm sunshine, good food, good company - a real break. So why don't they always turn out like that?

If you travel some 7 kilometres west from Xania along the northern coast of the island of Crete you will arrive in the seaside resort of Agia Marina where the apartments of Erofili are situated. They are looked after by Monica and her husband Manolis, whom I first met eleven years ago. The apartments were recommended to me by Ted and Rita Wareham and I have been thanking them ever since. Although over the years Agia Marina has increased in size it is still relatively unspoiled, with a wonderful beach and lots of excellent and inexpensive places to eat good Greek food.

Because it is still uncommercialised there is little to do during the day except walk the 10 yards or so from the apartment to the beach, arrange one's personal belongings in a suitable area, anoint each other with sun lotion and switch on the personal stereo and open a good 'holiday read'. Bliss! Unless of course you are accompanied by Jackie Brayshaw. Not for nothing is she known as Mrs Safety. Jackie is one of those people who have to check everything at least five times before she can leave the house. Is the gas turned off, TV unplugged, Neighbourhood Watch alerted, plumbers on stand-by and the windows and doors securely locked - and unlocked to check and re-locked? Have we all got our passports, tickets, luggage, spare wooden legs? On arrival the apartment must be inspected for potential hazards before we can unpack, then we can all relax because we know that Jackie will remain on guard, not just attending to our well-being but that of anyone who comes within her orbit.

Crete doesn't operate a 'nanny state' in the same way that Britain does but when the sea is really rough - so rough that nobody in their right mind would go anywhere near it - red flags are flown on the beaches. Unfortunately by three o'clock in the afternoon some idiots have had so much to drink that it's doubtful if they could see the flag never mind distinguish its colour. Stretching out from the beach in front of the apartments towards the island of

Agia Theodoris is a rough stone breakwater with a partly made-up path running along its length. On one particular afternoon in June 1992 I and most of the other folk on the beach were unashamedly asleep. Jackie wasn't of course. She was keeping a sharp lookout for 'hazards'. A group of Geordie lads wasn't wasting the afternoon in idleness either. They were awash with Greek lager and a match for any foreign waves, red flags or no red flags. Inevitably before long they were in trouble and being rapidly washed out to sea. Fortunately Jackie spotted them.

The first I knew of the drama was when I was rudely awakened by having my towel whisked from under me. Jackie was running down the beach tying together towels she had unceremoniously yanked from under other recumbent holidaymakers. Looking towards where she was heading I became aware of two men struggling in the sea. One had managed to catch hold of a rock at the end of the breakwater and was trying to climb out but the other was in real trouble. I ran after Jackie, hampered by the rough stone surface on my bare feet, already sore from the hot sand, but I managed to catch up with her and dissuade her from leaping into the water. Using the towels as a rope Jackie anchored herself to one side of the breakwater and by holding the other end I managed to lean over the other side and grab the wrist of the second man, who was being hurled against the rocks by the crashing waves. We both held on until Manolis, alerted by others on the beach, arrived with the Cretan lifeguards to give assistance.

Semi-conscious, the man was a deadweight, but he was eventually pulled from the sea, carried back along the breakwater and laid down in the centre of the crowd which had inevitably gathered to watch the drama. Although cold and slightly cyanosed (where the skin has turned blue through lack of oxygen) the victim was still breathing, albeit shallowly and irregularly, and he had a pulse. He also had a stomach full of beer and salt water and would almost certainly vomit before too long. Discretion certainly seemed to be the better part of valour in this case and, being a past master at the art of non-intervention, I turned him on his side, made sure his airway was clear and prepared to watch and wait.

It was at this point that a loud English voice interrupted the proceedings, demanding to be 'let through' as the owner of the voice was a nurse and knew exactly what to do. "Turn him over," she commanded, speaking slowly and loudly to the assembled foreigners. "Give him mouth to mouth respiration and cardiac massage." Obviously a fully qualified nurse! I'm certain she would have pushed me aside and carried out her threats to the cheers of the crowd - probably killing the victim in the process - if Jackie hadn't reared herself up to her full five foot three and, thrusting out her ample and still topless chest, made it quite clear that my friend is a doctor and knows exactly what he is doing thank you very much.' She emphasised the point by adding 'Go away.'

The Geordie lad had by this time, as predicted, vomited copiously all over the sand. He shook his head, sat up, said something comprehensible only to those born and bred north of the Tees, then got to his feet and staggered off back to his mates. He seemed to be completely unaware of how close to death he had come or of how Jackie had saved his life. She, however, was the focus of attention for the rest of the holiday, dubbed the heroine of the hour or, less respectfully, 'the little lady with the big boobies who saved the Englishman.' Even more gratifying was the endless supply of free wine with which she was plied at local Tavernas and which we shared as we basked in her reflected glory.

I mentioned in an earlier chapter that I don't like water and never really learned to swim very well, but I have tried hard not to let the phobia spoil my and other people's holidays. The year before the Cretan beach drama Kathleen and I were on holiday in the village of Born, near Villeréal, in a beautiful stretch of the French countryside between the rivers Lotte and Dordogne. We were staying in a farmhouse part-owned by Geoff and Judy Sargieson. Geoff was at that time Manager of BBC Radio Humberside and, as I said in the previous chapter, I was Chairman of the station's Advisory Board. The loan of the farmhouse for a two week holiday was a wedding present to Kath and I from Geoff and Judy. One of our fondest memories from that holiday was a day spent canoeing down the Dordogne from Souillac to Beynac, a distance of about 17 kilometres. Canoeing was perhaps an optimistic description of the experience as the water was so low that we had to carry the boats quite a bit of the time, walking on the rocks in the riverbed.

Two years later we returned to Born, this time with our friends Maggie and Paul from Liverpool and John and Jackie Brayshaw. We had enthused to them over the countryside, over the excellent wines, the magnificent meals, especially in the local Ferme Auberge, and of course the trip down the Dordogne and we were anxious to share all these delights with them - especially the trip down the Dordogne. John and Jackie opted to be spectators and taxi drivers while Maggie and Paul would accompany us in another canoe. Only this time it wasn't quite the same. The water looked different - was different. There had been violent thunderstorms in Eastern France and the river was in flood. The rocks were submerged, the water high up the banks and moving smoothly but rapidly down towards the sea, carrying debris along at quite a rate. We were assured by the canoe proprietor in Souillac that as we had canoed before and that provided we stayed in the centre of the river to avoid overhanging trees, our Canadian-style canoes were quite safe and would transport us rapidly downstream to Beynac. There were lots of canoes already on the river so I swallowed my misgivings, gratefully donned the compulsory lifejacket and comforted myself with the thought that Maggie had been a member of the Leicester University Canoe Club. Rather stupid as she was in another canoe.

We set off and once we had got the hang of synchronised paddling we had an uneventful journey to the bridge at Castelnaud which was almost halfway in our projected journey, and where we planned to have our picnic lunch, as it was one of the few places where it was possible to disembark. The Dordogne is joined at this point by the smaller river St Cion creating a small island. Needing to keep our wits about us we hadn't brought wine but we enjoyed an excellent meal, watching the water surging under the bridge on its way to Bordeaux. It was difficult to imagine a more peaceful setting but eventually we stirred ourselves, as we still had some 9 kilometres to paddle.

We repacked our bags, discussing as we did so how best to cast off, which route to take to the centre of the river and to which side of the island (which was about 10 metres out) we ought to go. To the far side the water was turbulent as it poured through the arches of the bridge, nearer to us it was calm and placid. The latter seemed to be the obvious choice as we had been watching with amusement as some of our fellow-picnickers had got into difficulties going round the long way. Kath and I set off first and felt quite proud of ourselves as we moved off from the bank, front end pointing downstream, paddling in unison as we aimed for the smooth water below the island from where we could get back into the middle of the river. Then in an instant everything was blotted out - light, sound - as we totally lost control and were sucked down, down into the depths of the river, spinning madly. The overwhelming sensation was of peace and tranquillity. Then just as suddenly we shot back up to the surface, from black to dark green, light green then brilliant sunshine. I was totally disorientated. All my worst nightmares come true. Where was Kath? Where was the canoe? Where were my glasses?! Panic spread through me.

With blurred vision I saw the upturned canoe to my left, spinning slowly. I still had a paddle in one hand. I must control my panic, I must get to the canoe. *Where was Kathleen?* I made a huge effort and kicked my way towards the boat, reaching for it with my free hand. Then I felt a hand, someone else's fingers clinging to the other side. It must be Kath - please let it be Kath. Coughing and choking I gasped 'Are you all right?' Stupid question - of course she wasn't all right. Neither of us was all right, we were drowning in a raging torrent and I could barely swim! We were being spewed down a flooded river clutching an upside-down boat watching our lunch box racing ahead of us towards Bordeaux and the open sea. And what about Maggie and Paul? We looked around and saw that they too were in the water and were clutching their upturned boat which was rotating slowly towards the edge of the calm water downriver from the island. What in heaven's name had happened? No matter. The important thing at this particular moment was survival.

I still felt totally disorientated, my confusion worsened by the loss of my glasses, a feeling I was later to remember when dealing with the early symptoms of post traumatic stress disorder in accident victims. We tried to right the canoe but as it was full of water it was very heavy and promptly overturned again, almost causing us to lose our hold. Kath said she was going to try to swim to the bank and told me to hold on while she got help. More panic. I pleaded with her not to go even the short distance from the canoe to the bank. It was dangerous and I needed her! She did try a few strokes but the current was too strong and realising the futility of it she grabbed the canoe again and we both clung on for dear life. Such stupid things go through your mind at moments like this. Here we were in mortal danger and I suddenly started to worry about our valuables. They had been stowed in a special waterproof box in Maggie and Paul's canoe. Were they even now rushing down the Dordogne with the remains of our lunch? No, as it happened. Fortunately when Paul had surfaced and clutched the nearest floating object for support it had been the safe box. Thank heaven for small mercies.

Meanwhile we were still speeding along in the middle of the river, held up by our lifejackets and at least able to talk to each other, to try to work out a survival plan, to regain control. At one point we managed to attract the attention of a motorist who had stopped on the road adjacent to the river to admire the view, but although he realised we were in trouble and drove alongside us for a while there was nothing he could do. We never did find out whether he actually tried to summon help. Paul and Maggie had been carried right across to the far side and were by now miraculously on dry land having washed up on one of the few flat sandy areas along that stretch. Mostly the banks are near vertical and muddy, the river in places 200 metres wide. There were quite a few other canoes paddling downstream and we yelled for help. 'Bonjour,' they shouted back, shaking their heads and laughing at our silly game. These English - what will they get up to next?

We were gradually being swept towards the bank on our left but it seemed to get steeper as we went downstream. Eventually by pushing with the paddle and kicking and struggling we managed to grab hold of an overhanging branch and pull ourselves right in under the steep bank. We were safe - well relatively. I threw the paddle up and it stayed on a little ledge. Kath jumped and landed in some rough shrubs and with me pushing from behind managed to haul herself up onto another little ledge behind a tree. I was still hanging onto the branch with one hand and the canoe with the other while she knelt above me yelling at me to let go of the boat and *jump* for goodness sake. But it wasn't our canoe. I couldn't just let it go. And anyway how would we escape without it? The bank above us was near vertical. But even as I debated with myself I knew that whatever happened nothing would persuade me to get back in that wretched canoe, not then or ever. And I never have.

Eventually I managed to hitch the canoe over a stump then climbed ashore and hauled it up a few inches out of the water before we both collapsed, exhausted, and tried to get our bearings and collect our thoughts. The main thing was we were safe - both of us, all of us - that was what mattered above all else in the world. We could still see Maggie and Paul some 400 metres away on the other side of the river. They had amazingly managed to right their canoe, empty out some of the water and were paddling downstream. Were they going for help? We had no way of finding out. The river raged beneath us and the rocky nettle-covered bank towered above us. What could we do? The only possible thing was to climb. We scrambled upwards for what seemed an eternity but was in fact only about 10 or 20 metres before we reached the top and found we were on the side of a road. Soaking wet, cold, exhausted and confused we just sat there. Again, stupidly, I started worrying about the canoe. How would the owners ever find it? Would we have to pay for it? Did I care?! I took off my lifejacket and tied it to a nearby tree as a marker. It was the best I could do.

It was then that through my blurred vision I saw a car parked on the roadside about 150 metres away. Its occupants were sitting on the bank having a picnic. Help - at last - was at hand. They turned out to be an English couple from the Wirral who must have been somewhat alarmed to see this bedraggled pair emerging from the bushes. They gave us a lift into Beynac where we were reunited with Maggie and Paul and were able to get in touch with the canoe's owners and explain about the lifejacket marker. Then we could take stock, count our blessings. We were all four intact - the most important thing. Paul had hung onto the watertight barrel containing our passports, credit cards and other valuables. I still had my camera round my neck. I can remember it being an immense weight when I was in the water but

I was determined not to let it go. Although I dried it out it was destined never to work again but we were insured and amazingly the majority of the photographs I had taken were able to be printed, albeit somewhat spotty!

The euphoria lasted until the next day when we were all very quiet as the realisation hit us of how close to death we had been. I think the most frightening aspect for me had been my total lack of control over the situation and of how badly I needed to talk to somebody about what had happened. Another lesson learned, to be remembered in future when dealing with the aftermath of a serious accident.

The incident didn't put us off holidaying in France and in 1998 we spent another very happy, relaxed and this time uneventful two weeks there. Until the journey home that is. We were on the road between Tulle and Clermont-Ferrand, the N89. The weather had been very mixed during the fortnight and was not good for the drive home. The road from Tulle climbs fairly steeply up into the hills below the Plateau de Millevaches. It was raining quite heavily and we realised something was amiss soon after leaving Tulle when two fire-engines, an ambulance and a fire-car with blue flashing lights joined the motorway from a slip road some way behind us. As we approached a bend on the brow of the hill some four or five kilometres east of Tulle we came across a horrendous accident. Two cars had apparently collided head-on and at some speed and we must have arrived no more than five minutes after it happened, just ahead of the fire-car. It was a scene of absolute chaos. People were milling around with no idea what to do and we felt obliged to stop.

In the first car the French female driver was trapped but conscious although quite unable to talk to me. Behind her in the rear off-side seat sat an elderly lady looking very peaceful but who was clearly dead. I went round to the other side of the car where the front seat passenger was also dead, having suffered extensive multiple injuries. The front seat had been pushed forward and completely crushed by the rear seat passenger who had not been wearing a seat-belt, highlighting warnings about the dangers of not wearing belts in the back seats of vehicles. There was also a young man in the back who was alive and conscious but obviously developing severe shock. There was nothing I could do for the other three but I told the fireman I was a doctor and he seemed quite grateful as no-one appeared to know what to do. I explained that two of the passengers were dead and that the driver was trapped and would probably take some time to release and that it would be better to concentrate first on getting the young man out.

I looked into the second car which had more or less disintegrated, killing the two occupants outright, so I went back to the young man. I tried to advise the firemen, who were doing a good job, but the victim was deteriorating rapidly. At that stage the medical team arrived and I witnessed some of the most ineffective attempts at roadside resuscitation that I have ever seen. I tried to convince the French doctor that the young man needed a drip setting up and a rapid infusion as a matter of urgency before being transferred to hospital as soon as possible if he were not to die from internal bleeding. I even offered to set up the drip but he declined and realising that I was just a useless observer I turned away in disgust and despair and drove away. I have nothing but praise for the firemen who followed my instructions about getting the victims out, protected the scene and controlled the onlookers. They were as good as the medical team were bad.

The trouble is that when you arrive at an accident like that with no equipment with you, however qualified you are, you are in fact no more use that an advanced first-aider. All you can do is make decisions on prioritisation, which I did, and apply the **ABC** of resuscitation.

The young man's **A**irway was unobstructed.

He was **B**reathing. He was conscious and had no obvious chest injuries so A and B were all right.

His **C**irculation however was certainly not and he was showing all the symptoms of rapid and increasing circulatory shock, about which I could do nothing without intravenous access and fluids.

As we drove off I reflected on the fact that there would in all probability be five fatalities from that one accident. The speed they must have been going in the atrocious conditions was just crazy. What really upset me as we left the scene were the bits and pieces of holiday luggage scattered around - handbags, suitcases, souvenirs - thrown from the cars on impact. Dead bodies, injured people I can cope with, they are after all part of my job, but the universally recognisable possessions of ordinary people going about their everyday lives, now so abruptly curtailed, painted an unbearably poignant picture. I felt a mixture of anger and grief, anger that not enough was being done to save the life of the young man who would become just another statistic and grief at the waste of life of people very like ourselves. There but for the Grace of God .... We drove very carefully for the remaining five hundred kilometres of our journey home.

As I said at the beginning of this chapter I have been fortunate enough during the course of my work to travel abroad fairly frequently to conferences, seminars and on lecture tours to places as diverse as New York, Washington, Sydney, Brisbane, Hong Kong and Bombay. On one such occasion I was on a flight to Crete in a rather cramped DC10 when a lady passenger had an epileptic fit. This was a prime example of the need to control an airway. When she went into the fit she was sitting up in her seat which as luck would have it was a window seat. This meant that in order to treat her we had to lift her over the other two seats into the aisle and carry her forward to find a freer space. Then it was simply a matter of lying her on her side, controlling her airway and giving her oxygen, with which the plane was well supplied. She soon came out of the fit, which was fortunate as the plane had very little else on board that would have been of use had she gone into 'status epilepticus', defined as someone who fits for longer than twenty minutes. At that stage the risk of complications and permanent brain damage rises dramatically in the absence of specialist treatment.

In another in-flight incident a call came over the Tannoy on a 747 jumbo-jet for a doctor and I and a young lady responded, going forward into the Club Class section. We were en-route for India and an elderly lady had been taken ill with severe breathing difficulties. She was pale and sweating and obviously in some distress. I knew that there were at least two colleagues of mine on that plane who were consultants but they were clearly keeping their heads down! The other doctor who had come forward was a Senior House Surgeon in the Accident and Emergency Department in Doncaster. She recognised me as a Consultant and said she would return to her seat as I was obviously quite capable of dealing with the emergency without her!

The incident occurred about a couple of months after the famous case when a passenger on a plane developed a pneumothorax, (that is when air leaks from a hole in a lung into the chest cavity, causing the lung to collapse) and a doctor on board had to make a hole in the patient's chest using a wire coathanger, a makeshift tube and a rubber glove! Lurid images flashed through my mind and I wondered why I had to be the one who volunteered.

By this time we were over southern Turkey, somewhere south of Istanbul. The next scheduled stop was Bombay, some two hours and ten minutes away. The practice of medicine in these circumstances becomes very basic. The noise from the engines made it almost impossible to hear any lung sounds but I coped with the situation by very gently and discreetly partially undressing her, then sitting her absolutely upright. This action alone seemed to help her, reassuring me that it was not a pneumothorax but that she was suffering from cardiac failure following a mild heart attack. She was able to talk a little and told me that she was on her way to Australia to stay with her nephew, that she lived in the West Riding of Yorkshire and that she had been unwell for a couple of weeks prior to travelling, suffering intermittently from shortness of breath. She also said that she had been prescribed 'heart tablets'.

It was a typical picture and by assessing the pulsation in her neck I could see that her jugular venous pressure was raised, confirming my opinion that I was dealing with cardiac failure. The problem was that the Singapore Airlines plane didn't seem to be carrying any useful drugs at all, just the usual plentiful supply of oxygen. I managed to get a venous line into her arm and the cabin staff eventually came up with some medication that contained Lasix, the trade name for frusemide, a diuretic which is one of the treatments for cardiac failure and I injected some of that. Contrary to popular belief doctors do not carry a complete pharmacy with them at all times any more than a plumber packs his blowtorch and a set of spanners when he goes on holiday.

Having administered very basic 'first aid' a decision had to be made as to what we were going to do next. The chief steward advised me to go and talk to the Captain, who was Indian, so I made my way forward through First Class to the cockpit where to my astonishment the Captain and his co-pilot were playing chess! That huge plane with five hundred plus passengers on board and umpteen crew was simply cruising along on auto-pilot. I discussed the situation with the Captain. The options were to turn round and go back to Istanbul, about half an hour away, request permission to land at Teheran, or go on to Bombay which would take another hour and fifty minutes. He wasn't keen to turn back and even less keen to put down in Iran so we decided on option three, my decision being influenced by the fact that the lady was 83 years old and her condition had improved since being given medication and oxygen.

I asked the Captain if I could use his telephone, on which he had just called his mother. I phoned my Consultant colleague and friend Guru Shirahatti at the Sion Hospital in Bombay where he is Dean and responsible for the Trauma Centre and within three minutes I was talking to him from 30,000 feet up requesting that a Flying Squad be waiting at the airport when we landed. The Captain was extraordinarily impressed that I was able to mobilise a medical team in India from a plane flying over Turkey.

For the next hour and three quarters I sat beside my patient with my fingers firmly crossed while Kathleen dozed happily on in her seat at the back of the plane, blissfully unaware of the dramas being enacted elsewhere. When we landed in Bombay the medical team dashed on board and the lady was whisked away to hospital. I never saw or heard from her again, neither thanks or acknowledgement. However I did get an extremely nice letter from Singapore Airlines along with a beautiful leather wallet, which I have to this day.

When I first started thinking about this book we had already decided to research some of my ancestors by visiting both America and Suffolk. The first time I went to America it was at the invitation of Ed McNeil. Ed was a Consultant in the Accident and Emergency Department in Westchester, New York County. His parents lived in Cottingham, on the outskirts of Hull and one day while he was on a visit to them he popped into the A & E Department at Hull Royal. We had an interesting chat, kept in touch after he returned home and eventually got to know each other quite well. In 1982 he invited me to address the New York Medical Society on 'Flying Squads in the UK'. This was an interesting choice of subject as the Yorkshire and East Riding Voluntary Accident and Emergency Service had by then been functioning for about fifteen years!

My second visit was ten years later, in May 1992, when Kathleen and I went to the States for our honeymoon. We spent the first week in Washington at the Biennial Joint Conference of the British Association of Emergency Medicine, and the second week staying with Ed McNeil at his home, Tishlub House, in Bedford County. Our intention was to seek out the Gosnold family connections in and around Boston, visiting Bartholomew's last resting place in Jamestown, Virginia. Unfortunately we got the wrong Jamestown, going instead to Jamestown Rhode Island! However, we did visit Massachussetts, Connecticut, and Martha's Vineyard.

Our first port of call was the town of Bedford and a museum where we signed the visitors' book under a bust of Bartholomew. We were greeted with open arms and shown the library archives. Our chief disappointment was that the ferry from Bedford to Cuttyhunk only ran on Wednesdays, and this was the Thursday of our final week. We did spend a long time in Martha's Vineyard though, searching through records in various museums and libraries and invariably being received like long-lost relatives. In one museum there was a painting depicting Bartholomew landing on a beach and meeting the Indians. We now have a copy of it hanging in the house in Lelley, next to an 1892 oil painting of Otley Hall.

We first visited Suffolk in 1989 and stayed in a B&B in a village near Otley. For our second expedition we took four days off and stayed at the Dove in Debenham. We had persuaded the then owner of Otley Hall, a Swedish entrepreneur by the name of Mosseson, to show us round the house which I described in the first chapter of this book. I took lots of photographs, only to realise later that there was no film in the camera! We also visited nearby High House, another family home of the Gosnold family (and this time I did successfully take photographs), and Otley Church with its memorial plaque and various other churches in the area where Gosnolds are buried. Finally we went to the Library in Bury St Edmunds where we were able to see the first known references to the Gosnold family in an entry in the Domesday Book.

As we were travelling back north to Hull from Bury St Edmunds on the A134 we came upon an accident in which a Mini was embedded underneath the cab of a lorry. Again we were first on the scene although an ambulance had been called. I was able with some difficulty to climb into the Mini, a hazardous operation as the air was filled with diesel fumes. The only occupant, a young lady, was trapped in the driver's seat, unable to move. She had a chest injury which was compromising her airway, obviously had several fractured ribs and was beginning to have difficulty in breathing. Kathleen will never forget that day as she was the only person available to assist me.

On this occasion I did have my medical bag in the boot of the car and this shows how different the scenario becomes when resources are available. The victim was conscious and able to speak and told me she was in great pain. Reaching across I was able to examine her chest superficially with one hand and could feel surgical emphysema, that is air leaking into the space under the skin which overlays the chest wall. As she was not in severe respiratory distress but clearly beginning to suffer from shock, the first priority was to put up a drip and Kath had to act as a drip stand! She held the bag up in her right hand while looking determinedly the other way as she has a total aversion to the sight of blood and would be of no use if she passed out. The drip was mainly to keep a vein open and replace fluid loss, as with such a significant injury it was likely that she was bleeding internally. I proceeded to put a drain into her chest cavity to release the trapped air outside her lungs and had just about completed it when the ambulance and Fire Brigade arrived. She was released from the car and taken first to Bury St Edmunds Hospital, then transferred to Cambridge. About a month later I received a letter from her. She had been in intensive care but was by then doing well and wrote a very nice letter of thanks enclosing a donation to our Accident and Emergency Endowment Fund. It turned out that she was a nurse at Bury St Edmunds Hospital.

Her chances of survival and recovery had been greatly enhanced because not only had I happened to be on hand, but I had equipment with me which enabled me to treat her immediately at an advanced level and not rely purely on basic first aid. She survived a major injury because I was able to replace her bodily fluids and protect her airway quickly, whereas I doubt whether the young man in France ever did. So much in life relies on fate, chance, luck - call it what you will - as well as skill.

A rather rough Mediterranean Sea off the beach of Agia Marina, Crete.

A distant view of Jackie and... well, you guessed it!

The Bougainvillea in full bloom over the front of Erofili.

Erofili from the beach.

The ambulance in case of emergencies in the Samaria Gorge, Crete. A little different to the ones in England!!

An idyllic Dordogne.

166

A rather different Dordogne in flood.

Preparing for the remainder of the journey with Maggie and Paul, shortly before the "immersion".

'THE OLD ORDER CHANGETH.......

As I contemplate my future and the future of medicine and the medical profession.

As I reach the final chapter of this book I have completed my twenty-fifth year in the Accident and Emergency Department of Hull Royal Infirmary and after a 'change in direction' have taken early retirement. I was honoured in my final year by being invited to be President of the Hull Medical Society - an exciting prospect in the millennial year and a pleasing culmination of a variety of honorary appointments over the years. Looking back it is difficult to single out any one experience that has given me the most pleasure or satisfaction but there are several I would like to mention because of their special significance.

Between 1985 and 1989 I represented the British Association for Accident and Emergency Medicine on the A&E Sub-committee of the Central Committee - quite a mouthful - chairing it when it became a sub-committee of the Central Consultants and Specialists Committee in 1989. In 1991 I was made an Honorary Senior Fellow of the University of Hull, Department of Social Studies, a post I proudly retain to this day. In return for giving a free lecture annually I have unlimited access to the wonderful Brynmor Jones Library. I was very honoured in 1992 to be invited to be President of the East Yorkshire Division of the British Medical Association, a very pleasing and convivial year of office.

In 1993 I sat and passed the Advanced Trauma Life Support Certificate, (ATLS), awarded by the Royal College of Surgeons. It was interesting because I was in competition with fourteen General Practitioners and two other Consultant colleagues from Hull Royal and no way was I going to be allowed to fail! In 1994 the Faculty of Accident and Emergency Medicine was inaugurated and those who had been Consultants for fifteen years or more were created Honorary Founding Fellows. It meant that I would never have to take the examination - a great relief. All these honorary appointments provided a basis for the exchange of ideas and information aimed at improving the efficiency of medical services throughout the country.

In 1994 I was also asked to act as Advisor to the Department of Health on the Tomlinson Report on the Reorganisation of Hospital Services in London. I was supposed to be the independent voice from the provinces! Visiting the capital took me right back to my student days. This was a real shake-up of the city's hospital services and there were bound to be casualties. The results are still moving through the system to this day. One of the things we had to advise on was the future of the A&E Department at Barts - St Bartholomew's Hospital. We advised in favour of closure, resulting in three of my colleagues being displaced and having to find posts in other London hospitals. I don't know whether they were ever aware that I was instrumental in them having to change their employment. In the same year I became Specialty Tutor at Hull Royal's A&E Department and a representative on the Yorkshire Regional A&E Training Committee. My mother would have approved.

Once you have been a member of an advisory committee word gets around. Since 1994 I have served as a member of the Accident and Emergency Casemix Group, advising the Department of Health, and also on the Advisory Committee on Accident Prevention in Children. These were prestigious appointments and I was very proud to be asked. I have also enjoyed the experiences and gained a lot from them.

My busiest time at Hull Royal was between 1989 and 1995 when I was Clinical Director of the A&E Department. It was a huge challenge as I was managerially responsible for all the doctors, nurses and ancillary staff, in fact everyone who was employed in the Department. In 1995 I moved on to be Clinical Co-ordinator and in the following year reverted to being a 'simple' Consultant in A&E.

With recognition in any field of medicine come requests for articles for medical magazines and presentations to seminars and conferences. One publication I remember particularly was an article on *'Confirmation of Death'*, for the British Medical Journal in 1980. At that time it was quite an important topic and I received a nice letter of acknowledgement from Professor Keith Simpson, the retired Home Office Pathologist and Professor of Forensic Medicine at Guy's Hospital and also of course one of the lecturers from my student days. I still occasionally dip into his autobiography, *'Forty Years of Murder'*. In the same year I contributed an article *'Spinal Cord Damage in Non-Accidental Injury'* to a journal called *Medicine, Science and the Law*. It was based on a case of a baby who died in Hull as a result of being shaken and it is still one of the causes of death in murdered children which largely goes unrecognised. In 1993 I was asked to contribute a chapter entitled *'Child Harm; Recognition and Management'* to a book on *'Injury; Diagnosis and Management in Accident and Emergency'*. This publicly confirmed my interest in non-accidental injuries to children and resulted in my giving a series of lectures on Child Harm to the Department of Social and Political Studies 'Diploma in Child Protection' course at Hull University.

I was also flattered to be invited to talk to an MRC Psychology Course in 1996 - a non-psychiatrist actually instructing psychiatrists for their higher qualification, my only qualification being a 'Section 12 Approved Doctor'. I had had a similar experience in 1993 when I was invited to give a lecture at the Royal College of Surgeons on *'Major Trauma - The Hull Experience'*, to an invited audience of UK surgeons. Me, a humble former GP, giving a lecture to surgeons on their home ground!

My many lectures abroad have given me immense pleasure, seeing new countries and meeting my opposite numbers who work in very different environments. The presentation of a paper on *'The Relationship Between Forensic Medicine and Accident and Emergency Medicine'* in the Great Hall of the International Conference Centre in Sydney in 1996 was an unforgettable experience, but I think above all I have enjoyed my visits to India in 1996 and 97. The audiences in Bombay are hugely appreciative and respectful as well as great fun. I have made many good friends and enjoy going back there more than anywhere else.

I think my most rewarding professional experience was during my time as Clinical Director of A&E at Hull Royal when we made a successful bid for special funding to develop a children's area in the A&E Department, which was at that time chosen as the National Demonstration Centre for the Treatment of Children in Accident and Emergency Departments. Hull Royal has frequently been at the forefront of developments and improvements in the care of patients, especially in the creation of a pioneering A&E Information and Technology system which has been copied all over the world. I am very proud of that.

In January 1999 I decided that it was time to slow down a bit. I reduced my A&E Consultant commitment by half and accepted a post as Director of Post-Graduate Medical Education for Hull and East Yorkshire. A fully-fledged teacher at last. My mother's dearest wish fulfilled.

On many occasions I have been asked how medicine has changed since I joined the profession in 1960 - almost forty years ago. I am really not allowed to say that 'it's not like it was in my day', but it's not. Nothing ever is or can be. The world does not stand still, but all progress is not necessarily for the better. I made reference in the chapter on my student days to the long working hours at St Thomas' and how during 'major weeks' we worked from one Tuesday lunchtime to the next without a break, and how stupid with tiredness we were by the end of it. Now Junior Doctors are not allowed to work more than fifty-six hours in any one week and must have regular breaks at the end of each shift. The downside to this is that not only do doctors in training not

170

get sufficient practical experience of clinical situations but also that it is difficult to balance the number of jobs available against the service requirements. It has affected the ability of the NHS to deliver an efficient service and has definitely affected the quality of training and the amount of exposure that Junior Doctors have to the practical aspects of learning medicine. There is no doubt at all that the theoretical teaching and the availability of training courses and lectures are vastly more organised than in my day but the result is young doctors with excellent theoretical qualifications but short of practical hands-on experience.

The financing structure of the Health Service is such that in some areas it is not possible to fund the number of doctors needed, which has led to excessive numbers of doctors being qualified in their specialties and hence to medical unemployment. The most classic recent example is in Obstetrics and Gynaecology where a lot of senior doctors are now trained but there are not enough senior posts available because of cash limitations.

In 1982 there was an important change in the Health Service when 'Unit Management Teams' were developed in Single District General Hospitals, but since then an even more significant change came with the NHS Reforms in 1992, which introduced Self-Governing Trusts. This brought increased responsibilities as well as freedoms. The NHS became far more accountable and the bottom line of the budget sheet had to balance. Money – or the lack of it – prevailed.

With the latest shake-up in 1998 came the development of Primary Care Groups, (now Primary Care Trusts) which have taken over from Fundholding General Practices and following the Bristol Enquiry the introduction of Clinical Governance and the National Institute for Clinical Excellence. Also with the recent legislation protecting 'whistleblowers' malpractice can be reported without fear of retribution. The position now is that not only are Trusts financially accountable but doctors will become much more *clinically* accountable for their actions and will have to base their treatments on 'evidence-based practice'. My own personal feelings are that the good doctors of the future will not really be allowed to act freely, using their own diagnostic skills and instincts, but will have to follow protocol and guidelines and that the practice of medicine will all become very standardised. Individual flair will have been taken out of medicine.

Other major changes which have occurred in the Health Service concern the nursing profession, which has altered dramatically. Nurses have become much more dominant in the delivery of clinical care with the development of Clinical Nurse Specialists and Nurse Practitioners. I would seriously question whether nurses these days really want to 'nurse' or whether they see themselves as 'mini-doctors'. I know this view is contentious but my worry is that the true 'profession' of nursing is being pushed into the background by the desire to carry out procedures that in the past have traditionally been the province of qualified doctors. Nurses are no longer coming into the profession straight from school to be taught their skills on the wards. They come in with University qualifications and great expectations but not necessarily with an understanding of what life is all about and a desire to make their patients' lives more tolerable by the provision of basic tender loving care. All is forgiven - bring back the State Enrolled Nurse!

The situation is however offset by the fact that when a good team develops with doctors and nurses working closely together, then that team is usually very good at delivering excellent all-round care. The crunch factor is that the Manager in charge of a department should have a real understanding of the delivery of complete medical practice and a considerable degree of empathy with the professionals who are responsible for delivering the clinical care. Sometimes this may mean taking a bit of a risk with the budget, but there is less flexibility within the new system for taking those risks. The NHS is bedevilled by the fact that budgets must balance at the end of each financial year which leaves very little scope for long-term planning. The other absolute is that I think the NHS is the last remaining political football and changes are often made only to score political brownie points.

In 1998 the National Health Service was fifty years old. I attended a celebration in Hull during which all those employees who had worked for the NHS for twenty-five years or more were presented with a rather nice anniversary clock inscribed with the words 'Royal Hull Hospitals NHS Trust'. 'Trust' - a far cry from the original concept of the NHS, just as 'A&E' is vastly different from the old Casualty Department. Indeed it was hard to realise that I was, technically speaking, doing the same job as I was twenty-five years ago. Phrases such as 'coping with change', 'keeping up to date', and 'revalidation' assume enormous significance.

There will always be a need for a place for people to go to in times of crisis and most of them immediately think of the local hospital 'Casualty Department', a term no longer used officially but still the popular name for A&E. 'Things' will always happen to people unexpectedly, in unexpected places, often far from home. Sometimes it is their own fault, sometimes the result of a fight or crime or just a plain accident. There will, sadly, also be 'major incidents' and the department must always be ready to cope, whether it be with a bewildered individual or a full scale emergency. They must

172

always be 'there' and I am pleased that I was a part of that.

It is interesting to look back over this book now that it is almost finished, now that the majority of the work is done, the memory bank plundered and the family interrogated. Most of it has been done while I have been on holiday when there were no interruptions from ringing telephones or bleeping bleepers, plenty of time to sit and think, reflect, remember. It has made me realise that anyone going into medicine, in particular A&E, must learn to tolerate interruptions, to work *with* the telephone, and learn to manage their time efficiently. Time must never be wasted, whether it is being used for work, play or relaxation. Time must be found for rest, for re-charging the batteries or 'burn out' will occur too soon. I think this is becoming increasingly important as the pressures for change in the NHS increase. I am even more aware now that I have retired of how intrusive and stressful the irregular routine and interruptive telephone calls can be. With the virtual eradication of many diseases such as tuberculosis and smallpox and the better management of cancer, heart disease and diabetes, people are living longer and the emphasis is changing from caring for the young and acutely sick to caring for the chronically ill and the old. I hope the NHS will still be there for me as I grow old.

But as many new rules are made, practices laid down and procedures standardised doctors must still rely on their senses. They must still use their eyes to *see* the whole situation. They must learn to *listen* to the patient and to witnesses to incidents. They must not be afraid to *touch* their patients - so many doctors these days seem to make a diagnosis from behind their desk. It's not a good idea to go around *tasting* things but *smell* is of vital importance. I have mentioned smells frequently throughout the book. They have always been very important to me. My Grandmother's strawberry jam and oriental souvenirs, my grandfather's creosote, they instantly bring back my childhood. Paraldehyde, which in the 'olden days' was the only 'safe' drug for the treatment of the acutely mentally disturbed, has a unique smell. It could only be administered through a glass syringe as it melted plastic and it is rarely used these days, but the smell will for ever remind me of Grandad Hartley and of my mother.

Hospitals no longer smell of - well - hospitals, (except in India where carbolic is still the most powerful odour) but they still have a distinctive smell, as do school dining halls. Sweaty feet remind me of my brother Tony who had awful trouble with his as a teenager. I have already said that I can never forget the smell of burning human flesh and death also has its own unique odour. A smell with a more modern significance is that of Petuli oil, used by drug addicts to camouflage the smell of illegal substances. Perhaps there is another book to be written about the significance of smells in medicine!

Finally there is the sixth sense, the one that tells you that someone is really ill even though you can't put your finger on specific symptoms, and this can be a life-saver. It is perhaps the most important sense of all, the one that singles out the doctor from the scientists.

To become a doctor you must really like people - all people. If the human body fascinates you but you don't like people you might as well settle for being a pathologist or a microbiologist.

Me? I like people.

Speaking on an Indian platform in 1996.

The "not so 5 star" accommodation I stayed in and loved! Part of the student accommodation at the Sion Hospital Medical School in Mumbai.

The entrance to the Casualty Department in Delhi through which Indira Ghandi was taken after she was assassinated. Unfortunately by the time she arrived there she was already dead.

A photo to mark the presentation of our clocks awarded to those staff who had managed to survive 25 years of working in the Royal Hospital NHS Trust. Karen Evans and Sue Catchpole, immediately in front of me, were two nurses who had supported me in the Accident and Emergency Department for most of their careers.

Appendix

Dr John K Gosnold M.B.B.S, M.R.C.G.P., D.Obst.R.C.O.G.,F.F.F.A.E.M., B.Sc.Hons.(Anatomy).
Qualifications, Career and Achievements

BORN 1942   10th March, Hornsea, East Yorkshire, England.

EDUCATION

1950-1960	Hymers College, Hull.
1960-1966	St.Thomas' Hospital Medical School, London.
1962-1963	University of London (Hon. Degree) (McSweeney Scholarship - Anatomy.)

QUALIFICATIONS:

1963	B.Sc.Hons (Anatomy)	University of London.
1966	M.B.B.S.	University of London.
1968	D.Obst. R.C.O.G	University of London.
1975	M.R.C.G.P.	University of London.
1994	F.F.F.A.E.M	Royal Colleges of London, Edinburgh and Glasgow.

APPOINTMENTS:

1975	Consultant in Accident & Emergency, Hull Royal Infirmary.
1982	Forensic Medical Examiner, Humberside Police.

HONORARY APPOINTMENT

1991	HON. Senior Fellow, Department of Social Studies, University of Hull.

EMPLOYMENT HISTORY:

1969	General Practice, Hedon & York.
1975	Consultant, Accident & Emergency, Hull Royal Infirmary.
1989-1995	Clinical Director, Accident & Emergency, Hull Royal Infirmary.
1980-1998	Section 12 Approval, Mental Health Act.
1992	Named Doctor, Child Protection, Royal Hull Hospitals NHS Trust.
1999	Director, Postgraduate Medical Education, Hull and East Yorkshire.

ACADEMIC APPOINTMENTS

1989	Course Organiser, North of England Induction Course.for Senior House Officers in Accident & Emergency.
1993-1998	Member of Regional Specialty Advisory Committee in Accident & Emergency.
1993	Advisor to the Department of Health Health of the Nation Paper on Accident Prevention.
1994	Advisor to the Department of Health Tomlinson Report on Reorganisation of Accident Services in London.
1995-1998	Specialty Tutor, Accident & Emergency, Hull.

MANAGEMENT TRAINING

1992	General Management Training Course, Ashridge Management Training College.
1995	Appraisals Skills Course, Yorkshire Region.

SPECIAL PROJECTS

1991	National Demonstration Centre for Child Care in Accident & Emergency.

1991	Comparator Study - Evaluation of Major Trauma Centres in the UK.
1994	Development of a Training Programme for Nurse Practitioners in Accident & Emergency.
1998	Advisor to the L.T.M.G. Medical College, Mumbai, on 'Trauma Services in Mumbai'.

PROFESSIONAL COMMITTEES

1986-1990	Chairman, Hull Royal Acute Medical Committee.
1988-1991	Vice-Chairman, Humberside Child Protection Committee.
1995	Chairman, Royal Hull Hospitals Child Protection Committee.
1988-1992	Chairman, Training Sub-Committee Humberside Child Protection Committee.

RESEARCH PROJECTS

1. D.H S S Co-operative Study on the Results of the Introduction of Seat Belts in the
2. Alcohol and the Financial Effect on the NHS, Institute of Nursing Studies, University of Hull.
3. Major Trauma Outcome Study: An Analysis of the Outcome in Patients suffering from Major Trauma in the UK
4. Accidents in Children. A joint research study in Hull and York on the Epidemiology of Accidents in Childhood
5. Clinical Advisor to the Department of Clinical Psychology for various Projects involving the University and the Accident & Emergency Department

PUBLICATIONS

1991	Gosnold, Williams. An improved method of communication between computerised A&E Departments and General Practitioners.
1993	Gosnold et al. Methaemoglobinaemia as a result of Sodium Nitrate poisoning.Arch. Emerg. Med.
1993	Gosnold, Reynard et al. SHO Training. Assessment Initiative in Accident & Emergency.BMJ
1993	Development of Brief Learning Materials for Junior Doctors. Joint Centre for Education

TEACHING

1. Institute of Nursing Studies. Major Trauma.
2. Department of Social and Political Studies. Diploma in Child Protection. Lectures on Child Harm
3. Postgraduate School of Medicine, University of Hull, Department of Psychiatry, M.R.C. Psychiatry Course. 'The Management of Deliberate Self Harm.
4. 1996 L.T.M.G. Medical School, Mumbai. The Organisation of Trauma Services in the UK.
5. 1997 Alumni Association in Social Studies, Tata Memorial Hospital, Mumbai. 'Modern Technology: its use in planning Accident & Emergency Services'.
6. 1998 A.I.I.M.S. Delhi. Keynote Address to an International Conference on the Management of Major Trauma in the UK.

SPECIAL INTERESTS

Member of the Joint Committee on Higher Training, Accident & Emergency.
Yorkshire Regional Representative, British Association for Accident & Emergency Medicine.
Member of the National Accident & Emergency Casemix Group, National Casemix Office.
Past President, East Yorkshire Division, British Medical Association.
President, Hull Medical Society, 1999-2000
Chairman, BBC Radio Humberside Local Radio Advisory Council, 1989
Medical Officer to Hull R.L.F.C.; Hull Kingston Rovers R.L.F.C.; Hull R.U.F.C.
Snooker - to a standard sufficient to reach the semi-final of the Hull City Handicap Cup, 1991!
Exercise - to a level which still takes me to the Fitness Centre at least twice a week.

John Kenelm Gosnold was born in Hornsea in 1942 and can trace his ancestors back to 1066 when one of them really did come to England in the wake of William the Conqueror! The most famous member of the family was Captain Bartholomew Gosnold who sailed to the New World at the behest of Queen Elizabeth I and named one of the islands he discovered 'Martha's Vineyard'.

John himself has had an interesting and colourfully varied career, studying medicine at the famous St Thomas' Medical School after ten years at Hymers College in Hull. He was a partner in General Practice in Hedon in the late 1960s, followed by four years running his own practice in York.

From 1975 he worked in the Accident and Emergency Department of Hull Royal Infirmary, in charge of the team which dealt with the Lockington train disaster and for many years 'on call' with the Helicopter rescue service. Also, uniquely, he has been Honorary Club Doctor with both of the city's Rugby League clubs.

With a long list of publications to his credit he is regularly invited to lecture all over the world especially on child abuse, in which field he has pioneered procedures now universally recognised and adopted.

The Little Red Bike is a lively account of his professional and private life, from a milk round in Rolston to the start of his retirement, which he has taken early. He prefers to call it 'a change of direction'.

Margaret Garbett is a freelance journalist who lived in Hull for forty years during all of which time she was married to Peter, a master at Hull Grammar School, who died in 1992.

Margaret worked for BBC Radio Humberside for over twenty-five years, during which time she met John, and also Ernie Teal, the subject of her previous book, *'The Heydays' (Hutton Press)*. She edited NADFAS News, the magazine of the National Association of Decorative and Fine Arts Societies, for ten years up to 1997 and was then Administrator of the British Association of Friends of Museums until she retired in May 2000.

In 1993 Margaret moved to Winsley, a village in Wiltshire, to be nearer to her family. She has three married children and three grandchildren. She is very involved in the local community, especially as a volunteer in the Dorothy House Hospice in Winsley. She is also a part-time House Manager at the Wiltshire Music Centre in Bradford-on-Avon.